James Frank Smith Learner was born in the small town of Wembley Hill, Middlesex, in 1917 — the third year of the Great War.

He was educated at Quainton Hall School in Harrow and at the Lower School of John Lyon also in Harrow, before leaving at the age of 15 to become a student at Selfridge's Store in Oxford Street.

From 1938 he worked in his father's overall manufacturing firm in the City of London until the outbreak of the Second World War.

Joining H.M. Forces he served with The Buffs (the Royal East Kent) Infantry Regiment and saw action in Alamein until invalided out to spend the remainder of his Army service in a Forces Entertainment Unit in Cairo.

After the war he joined the Civil Service spending an equal number of years in the former Post Office Savings Bank and in the former Telephone Manager's Office.

He and his family left Wembley Hill in 1929 and moved to Hatch End in Middlesex. He married Lilian in 1949, then lived in Ealing in West London until 1980.

On his retirement in 1980, they moved to the tranquil village of Grange-over-Sands, in Cumbria, to enjoy walking, cycling, chess and writing.

Dedicated to my brother John whose idea it was
I should write this book.

A COLD BATH
EVERY MORNING

by
JAMES LEARNER

OWL
BOOKS

First published November 1992
by
Owl Books,
P.O. Box 60,
Wigan WN1 2QB

ISBN 1 873888 30 9

Designed and typeset by
Park Design and Print, Wigan.

Printed and bound in Great Britain.

Text typeset via DTP 11.5 on 13.5pt ITC Clearface
using 800 d.p.i. laserprinter.

CONTENTS

ACKNOWLEDGEMENT

Points from *A History of Wembley* by courtesy of the
London Borough of Brent Leisure Services Department

Prologue

IN the early 1920s in a snug little terraced house on a steep hill lived the Learner family—Edward and Emma and their three sons and a daughter (ages ranging from 8 to 14) who led a placid existence in the quiet, peaceful township of Wembley Hill.

From the balcony of their home in Linden Avenue they delighted in a panoramic view of green fields, magnificent old oak trees and the spacious grounds of Wembley Park.

Horse-drawn omnibuses were only just starting to be withdrawn from service. Ubiquitous GENERALS of the London General Omnibus Company, open and closed top trams and a few cheeky pirate buses comprised the usual forms of transport for the local populace. The favourite walk of the Learner family was 'down Raglan Gardens', a twisting, narrow, dusty country lane leading into Wembley Park Drive. The children played their endless games in King Edward the Seventh Park, strolled round the bandstand on summer evenings listening to martial music, or rolled over and over down a steep, grassy bank to see who could roll the furthest.

This idyllic existence was shattered with the building of the Wembley Empire Stadium almost literally on their own doorstep. At the same time buildings were being erected for the British Empire Exhibition. Their beloved Raglan Gardens was transformed slowly but inexorably into a wide busy thoroughfare soon to be known as Empire Way.

Wembley Hill Road at the bottom of Linden Avenue, normally a quiet road used mainly by horse-drawn carts and vans, was turned almost overnight into a highway teeming with cars, char-a-bancs, buses, taxis and a variety of other vehicles all making their way to stadium or exhibition.

These conditions in Wembley Hill, combined with the fact that the Learner house was 'bursting at the seams' with four fast- growing children, led Edward Learner to the inescapable conclusion that they would have to move to pastures new.

Each and every member of the Learner household knew that the glorious golden days of their beloved Wembley Hill were gone for ever.

BOOK ONE

Introducing Jim Learner

"Hey!" Watch where you're going, young feller me lad.
You nearly bowled me over".

THE elderly gentleman frowned down at the boy who had run almost full tilt into him. The boy startled, looked up guiltily at the speaker. "Sorry, sir, I wasn't looking where I was going", and added politely: "Hope I haven't hurt you?"

"It's all right, me boy, just be a bit more careful", replied the old man as he went on his way, hat pulled down and coat collar turned up to protect him from the elements.

It was raining heavily and the wind was gusting strongly. On such an evening the majority of folk were glad to be cosily indoors, eating muffins or roasting chestnuts in front of a roaring fire. Late autumn leaves were strewn on roads and pavements. With each swirl of wind they were scooped up as if by an invisible hand and dashed into the faces of passers by.

Some would look annoyed and brush the leaves aside with a muttered curse but Jim Learner took it all in good part. He laughed inwardly as he skipped along Wembley High Road oblivious of leaves, wind, rain and anything else that might be thrown at him on his journey to the church hall. He was overjoyed to see some of the shops already had sprigs of holly, silver tinsel and little tufts of cotton wool festooned around their window displays. Christmas was only a few weeks off.

Jim was eight years old but looked older. Sturdy of frame, his winter coat was several sizes too big for him and his stout boots were proof against all types of weather. He wore a brand new Cubs cap of which he was inordinately proud. He liked this so much better than the red woollen pom-pom hat his mother made him wear to go to school. Under his overcoat he wore his Cubs uniform complete with scarf, woggle, badges and company name blaze. His mother had said before he set out on the journey: "Don't go jumping into puddles and kicking stones about. Your father won't be able to afford another uniform like that for a long time".

Jim was a good lad who, considering his tender years, knew very well the struggle his parents had keeping themselves, his two brothers and his sister properly fed, clothed and educated. When playing with local boys, coming home from school or going to the pictures he was happy and contented. But however much he was enjoying himself he frequently had a mental picture of his snug little home on the hill. He loved his parents and got on reasonably well with his older brothers and sister. He was never happier than when playing with his No. 1 Meccano set in a bedroom shared with his brother John or when making mud pies in the back garden.

Continuing his erratic path along the High Road he was filled with wonder and excitement at all the sights and sounds around him. He stopped to press his nose against the baker's window, his mouth watering as he peered at mounds of macaroons, fairy cakes, chocolate eclairs and iced buns.

Then he caught sight of a coal cart lumbering its way towards him. There were still a few bags of coal stacked at the back of the cart but the load was mostly made up of neatly heaped empty sacks. The sight and smell of coal always made Jim think of their coal shed at home. This, together with carbolic soap, paraffin oil, gas mantles and cooking pots on the kitchen range were all part and parcel of the comfortable smells of home.

Steeped in these thoughts and aromas Jim was startled by the shouts of the coalman as the huge carthorse stumbled on the wet cobbled street. A tram was thundering by, the driver stamping repeatedly on the bell pedal. The frightened animal reared up in the shafts; it looked as if it was about to bolt.

People walking nearby scattered, terrified as the coalman scrambled down from his seat. He grabbed hold of the reins and tried desperately to calm the sweating animal, but his hands were cold and wet. He abandoned the reins and fumbled to get a grip on the slippery bridle.

He couldn't do it and — horrors — his right hand and wrist got caught inside the frantic animal's mouth. He yelled and screamed with pain. Bystanders pointed and shouted but nobody dared get near the animal to help. It looked as if the horse would sever the coalman's arm. Every time the poor fellow pulled in a desperate attempt to get his arm free, so the horse's head shot up and down.

It was just about to bolt when a man carrying a heavy walking stick rushed up to its side. Reaching up he delivered a sharp rap on the bony part of the horse's head, which caused the animal to bellow with pain and the scared and weakened coalman was able to wrench his arm free.

The man with the walking stick was obviously used to taking firm sensible action. Dropping his stick, he got hold of both sides of the bridle and, making soothing sounds, managed to calm the animal down. Jim was only a few feet away from him on the opposite side of the road, but was very frightened and being a sensible lad, knew there was nothing he could to to help.

He started to run the four or five hundred yards to the church hall but instinctively stopped to peer for the umpteenth time at the fascinating display in the window. It was on the frontage of a small office of the local coal merchants, the Tyne Main Coal Company.

The premises were set back off the main road in a little crescent into which carts, lorries and various other vehicles could stop and load or unload their goods. In the centre of the crescent was an opening which led into the forecourt of the town's main railway station.

Jim was very familiar with this crescent. Whenever he had the opportunity he would venture into the forecourt and observe with fascination the sights and sounds of trains arriving and departing and passengers hurrying to and fro.

But in the High Road at this moment his whole being was concencentrated on the coal agency's display. There were a few little wicker baskets filled with various types of coal and coke. Some had small nuggets of shining black coal, whilst on paper mats on the floor of the window were large hunks of untreated coal. Jim was not really interested at this aspect of window dressing. His gaze was riveted on a very lifelike model of the surface workings of a coal mine. He saw the pit head, the gantry with cables moving up and down on the gantry wheel, tiny iron buckets emptying their loads onto beautifully proportioned coal carts drawn by many different coloured horses, and little tiny men with blackened faces urging the horses onto the moving road surface. This surface would revolve round the centre of the display.

Jim would wait eagerly for the various coal carts, horses and drivers to emerge from the back of the model and continue their endless cycle around the colourful display. It was a wonderful scene which he knew he would want to look at again and again.

"Hey, Jim come on. Stop day dreaming. Give us a hand with this cart".

Looking round guiltily Jim saw three members of his wolf cub pack trundling a trek cart along the roadside at a very fast pace. He ran forward, grasped one side of the cart and grinning at his friends, strained eagerly towards the cart's destination.

Turning off the High Road and running down the short stretch of hill to the church hall, they all now pulled back on the trek cart to prevent it running away from them. It was a sturdy two- wheeled vehicle with a long shaft at one end. Similar vehicles were in use by cubs and scouts all over the world.

They turned into the short driveway inside the church grounds. As the others began to unload the cargo of groundsheets, tools and other items they were going to use for practising the erection of tents, Jim watched them for a few seconds. He was inclined to be introspective. Although he was very happy and contented in becoming fully involved in his cub activities, always at the back of his mind was the picture of his father, mother, brothers and sister, all happy in their own way, living together in a contented and harmonious household. But now he was eager to enjoy himself with his pals in the hall.

With a shout he leapt up the steps of the church hall and ran inside to be welcomed with the familiar yells of 'akela', 'wolf', 'dyb - dyb - dyb' 'dob - dob - dob'. For a couple of hours he was a part of the happy and carefree atmosphere which he had looked forward to all week.

Letchworth

I N the early 1920s the people of Great Britain had settled down to a period of relative peace and reasonable prosperity. Everyone was trying to forget the ravages of war. And the people of Wembley Hill were no exception.

Geographically Wembley Hill was roughly in the centre of a number of towns — Harrow, Sudbury Town, Greenford, Perivale, Alperton, Stonebridge Park, Kingsbury and Kenton. All the shopkeepers, bankers, insurance agents, solicitors, milkmen, road sweepers and every private citizen living in these towns, all wanted desperately to be allowed to get on with their lives without interference.

The peaceful, quiet, countrified little township of Wembley Hill was the home of Edward and Emma Learner and their four children. They lived in a sturdily built terraced house called Letchworth on a steep hill; in fact it was the hill which gave this particular part of Wembley its name. From the front balcony of their home in Linden Avenue they could look out onto a pleasant panorama of open fields and woods. Not more than a quarter of a mile distant was a large field on which the Learner children played and had the occasional picnic.

Linden Avenue and its two neighbouring avenues, Dagmar and Mostyn, all had the same thing in common. They were pretty steep and each opened out at the top onto common land from which there was a magnificent view of King Edward the Seventh recreation ground. Each of these avenues contained some forty or fifty terraced houses built around the turn of the century. They were tenanted by what were termed 'good class' families.

Edward Learner owned and controlled a factory in the City of London manufacturing doctors' and nurses' uniforms, boiler suits, dungarees and other types of protective clothing. One immediate neighbour was important in legal circles; another was Chief Clerk in one of the local banks.

With few exceptions everyone was on friendly terms with his neighbour. One such person was a woman living at the very top of Linden Avenue. She and Emma Learner got on very well despite the fact that the woman was inclined to be rather 'poshly' dressed and her make-up, in Mrs. Learner's view, was somewhat excessive. She sent her children into fits of laughter when she said the woman looked as if she had dipped her face in the flour bin.

Occasionally a motor-car or a motorised tradesman's van chugged slowly up the avenue, emitting a noxious blue cloud of burnt oil. But normally deliveries of milk, bread and groceries were made by horse-drawn vans or hand-pushed carts. The poor horses were hard put to it, struggling up the steep incline.

The baker's roundsman was the definite favourite of the Learner children. Upon completion of his deliveries at the top of the avenue, he turned the van round and coaxed the reluctant horse to attempt the quite dangerous descent, slipping and clattering over the uneven surface.

On wet days the unfortunate beast's legs would give way; only protracted and vehement shouts and curses from the baker would succeed in getting the horse on the move again. To calm the excited animal he would pull his van over to the side of the road and stop outside Letchworth.

The baker positioned the van's wheels against the curb at an angle to prevent the vehicle running out of control down the hill. The horse would mount the pavement just far enough for his head to be hanging over the front gate of Letchworth. With cries of excitement and delight the children came running out of the house clutching lumps of sugar for their beloved 'Prince'.

The sugar lumps exhausted, one or other of the children begged to be allowed to ride down the hill beside the baker 'in the driving seat'. They wanted to watch Prince in action. If the baker was in a good mood he swung them up onto the hard wooden seat and told them to hold on tight. Their joy knew no bounds. Grasping the reins the baker coaxed his horse to continue the hazardous passage down the remainder of the hill.

The children never failed to be fascinated by the sight of the horse's rump swinging to and fro in the van's shafts. At the bottom of the hill they clambered down from the van and with shouted thanks to the baker, ran back home as fast as they could to tell their mum all about it.

* * * *

The Learners could truthfully be described as a very close-knit family. There was never any suggestion of resentment or annoyance at the somewhat crowded conditions in their compact little house. Jim (the baby) and his middle brother John (two-years older) shared one of the back bedrooms overlooking the tiny garden. John was the bright one of the four children. He was frequently in trouble at school for facetious behaviour, but this was offset by his above-average scholastic abilities. He was now an enthusiastic Boy Scout.

Ruth, a month or two past her twelfth birthday, liked to be left to her own devices as much and as often as possible. A strongly- built dark-haired girl, she was mad on school sports and was forever leaving her hockey stick leaning against the hall-stand for someone to trip over. She occupied the smaller bedroom at the front of the house and was able to observe all activities in Linden Avenue from her bedroom window.

The eldest brother, Peter liked to hold himself aloof from the activities of his younger sister and two kid brothers. Very tall and skinny he was now in his fourteenth year and was the studious member of the family. He frequently took it upon himself to take young Jim to task for actual or alleged misdemeanours, and would show his annoyance if he caught one or other of the little so- and-sos sneaking into his bedroom. Peter took great pride in telling visiting aunts or uncles that his bedroom was ' next to my parents' room'.

Edward and Emma Learner occupied the largest bedroom (also at the front of the house) which boasted a small balcony. These four bedrooms, together with a large and commodious airing cupboard, a bathroom and toilet comprised the first floor of the Learner household.

* * * *

Downstairs there was a long draughty passage somewhat grandly called the hallway. Even on a bright sunny day this passage was dark and cheerless. Being one of the middle houses in a long series of terraced dwellings there were no side windows to give light to much of the Learner home. Had it not been for a skylight placed at the front part of the Letchworth roof – similarly to be found in all the other houses in the avenue – the gloom in the hall downstairs would have been even more apparent.

All the rooms on the ground floor were small. On the left of the passage was the door to the withdrawing room. Mrs. Learner who, although certainly no snob, liked her friends and neighbours to know that she was aware of the social graces. She insisted on speaking of the withdrawing room rather than the drawing room or living room. It was kept constantly spotless, under wraps and undisturbed except for rare occasions – high days, Holy Days and visits from Mr. and Mrs. Wyatt, next door neighbours who came in two or three times a year for an evening of music and verse.

Mr. Learner played the piano—a beautiful upright—with great feeling and accomplishment. Often when the younger children had been packed off to bed, they would lie awake and listen to many of their favourite pieces being beautifully played by their father; such haunting melodies that would be recalled and loved by them for many years to come.

The children were also banned from the withdrawing room when the Wyatts came in for the evening. Henry Wyatt was short, stocky and inclined to pomposity and was encouraged to recite whole long passages from one or other of the classics. His voice was unkindly referred to by Ruth as 'like a foghorn'; whilst Harriet, Henry's wife, sat timidly in the corner of the room making appropriate clucking noises of approval whenever she was wide awake enough to do so.

She longed for the interval when tea and sandwiches were brought in. The plates, cups and saucers were of a very delicate Chinese pattern which Harriet knew only came out on special occasions and had been brought over to England by Mr. Learner's sister and her husband. They were missionaries in China and had brought many Chinese and Formosan gifts back to the old country on their furloughs. Many of these exquisite articles were tastefully displayed in the glass fronted cabinet in one corner of the room.

A delicate octagonal table inlaid with mother-of-pearl was always placed in front of Harriet for her teacup and plate. She was terrified lest a disaster befell the china or the table. Refreshments disposed of, the distinctly highbrow evening invariably closed with a polished performance of a Chopin etude. The Wyatts never failed to express their fulsome appreciation of Mr. Learner's virtuoso recitals.

Continuing down the passage of Letchworth, the second door on the left opened into the dining-room. This room, like the hallway, was dark with only a limited amount of light penetrating the interior. A narrow passage between Letchworth and the neighbouring house had a paucity of light which was the reason for the gloominess of the Learner's dining-room. The children played games in this confined space which was unashamedly referred to as the back yard. An old galvanized iron bath tub hanging on a rusty nail was the sole object to grace this play area.

Returning to the dining-room, on the infrequent occasions when it was used for dining, resort had to be made either to flaring gas mantles fixed on two of the walls, or to a handsome brass oil lamp. The latter was kept in a permanently pristine condition by one or other of the children; who took turns to polish it on a strictly rota basis.

In the centre of the room which measured only twelve feet by ten feet was a solid oak dining table. There were four straight- backed light oak dining chairs, two on each side of the oblong table, and a similar chair, with arms, at the head of the table. The table and chairs practically filled the dining-room and a Singer sewing machine had pride of place on a massive sideboard.

Three reproduction paintings depicting scenes of Welsh hills valleys adorned the walls. One such scene was of Penmaenmawr where Mr. and Mrs. Learner had spent their honeymoon. A triple shelved bookcase was fixed on the wall between sideboard and window. A permanent aroma of paraffin oil, beeswax and Mansion polish pervaded the whole room, and without them the Learners would have wondered what was missing from the atmosphere of their home. Occasionally the children could play certain approved card and other games on the dining-room table, or Jim and John were permitted to make model trucks, cranes and railway rolling stock from their Meccano Sets.

At the far end of the hall passage were the kitchen and scullery. The kitchen was the focal point of the Learner household. It was lived in in every sense of the word. The family's everyday activities; discussions, children's arguments, occasional misfortunes or strokes of luck, were played out in the smoke- filled, steamy, homely atmosphere of their well-loved dear old kitchen.

Practically the whole of one side of this was taken up by the kitchen range, a masterpiece of engineering and a constant source of worry and work to Mrs. Learner who laboured ceaselessly to keep it clean. (Black-leading the range and whitening the front step were the bane of her existence). It was jet black in common with the huge kettle, pots, pans and other cooking utensils always to be found stewing or simmering something or other on its surface.

A large deal table some eight feet long and four feet wide stood under the kitchen window, and three varnished kitchen chairs of equally solid manufacture, two or three small stools and a venerable rocking chair comprised the seating accommodation for the family.

The dresser, which stood adjacent to the table, was a large, commodious affair brought to Wembley on the occasion of the Learner's marriage. It had been in use in Mr. Learner's parents home for donkey's years before being transferred to Letchworth. In dark oak, it reached to the ceiling and had numerous shelves, cubby-holes, cupboards and drawers all crammed with plates, tureens, gravy dishes, huge meat servers and a variety of cups, saucers, glasses, jam pots and every imaginable size and shape of jug.

The incredible thing was that despite constant use by so many different individuals, every shelf and drawer was kept in apple pie condition mainly due to Mrs. Learner's efforts. Woe betide any child (or husband) who failed to put things back in their proper places. The floor was covered with well-worn linoleum. The only concession to creature comfort was a strip of coconut matting stretching the whole length of the kitchen floor. As in the rest of the houe lighting came from gas mantles, oil lamps and candles in sconces placed over the mantelpiece.

There were two doors in the kitchen. One from the hall passage and one leading into the scullery (or back kitchen) and from there into the back garden. Upon entering the scullery anybody looking in for the first time would be immediately struck by two things: an enormous copper boiler set in concrete in one corner of the room and the overpowering smell of washing.

Every day was wash-day for Emma Learner. She rarely complained because she knew the work had to be done. Perspiration dripped from her brow and she was forever pushing stray locks of hair back into place. She wielded a foot-long wooden pole in and out of the boiling water in order to turn the mass of washing over and over. The grate under the boiler was fed with coke or coal. Stray lumps of coke sometimes escaped from the furnace and were trodden on by thoughtless children coming in from the garden. Infuriated, she would shout at the culprit: "Look at my floor. Now go back in the garden and stay there until I want you".

The capacious larder, despite the close proximity to the boiler, managed to remain cool in all seasons. Cooked meats stood on oval dishes covered with gauze cloths; hams, cheeses, mounds of butter later to be fashioned into small rolls using wooden plats, strings of onions hung from shelf hooks, bread in white enamelled BREAD bins, willow pattern tea caddies, sugar tins and a wonderful variety of bottled plums, raspberries, blackcurrants, gooseberries and home made marmalade. Muslin bags hung, heavily filled with crab apples and sugar, to make the children's favourite jelly. Food in the shops was reasonably cheap. Seven large eggs cost 7d. Butter was a shilling a pound and sugar sixpence a pound. The Learner larder was always well stocked.

The kitchen sink was situated in one corner of the scullery. There was very little room for the washer of dishes as the sink stood cheek by jowl with the copper boiler. With Mrs. Learner or Ruth standing at the sink washing the crockery and with a very inadequate draining board, the dishes and cutlery piled up on the draining board quicker than the wipers-up could deal with them. There was no flat surface in the cramped conditions of the scullery; consequently every item had to be carted into the kitchen and stacked on table or dresser. But this was only part of the trouble. With the boiler in almost constant use, the hot water for washing up had to be brought in pans or kettles, often scalding hot, from the kitchen range.

All these inadequacies, short-comings and trying conditions throughout the household were accepted by parents and children alike. They grumbled, they argued, they sometimes scrapped (at least the children did) but overall they were happy and contented. The youngsters were old enough to observe the abiding love their parents had for each other. For their part Mr. and Mrs. Learner were proud of their happy breed. They would always do their utmost to bring up their children in a humble, decent, God-fearing atmosphere.

A Cold Bath

EDWARD Learner stirred restlessly in his bed, struck a match, lit the candle, looked at his gold hunter watch on the bedside table, satisfied himself that it was precisely 5.30 a.m. and climbed stiffly out of the matrimonial bed. Approaching forty, he was tall (a little over six feet) slim, wiry and prematurely bald. A sparseness of brown hair could be seen at the back of his head and at the temples.

Donning a plain dark brown woollen dressing-gown over his long flannelette nightshirt, he opened the bedroom door, and carried the flickering candle along the corridor to the bathroom. Finding a box of matches in its accustomed place on the marble-topped bathroom cabinet, he struck a match and lit the gas mantle which was fixed to the wall immediately over the full-length mirror.

He sluiced face and neck with cold water from the basin, dried those parts vigorously with a rough towel and then, still using cold water, had a shave. Quickly wiping off surplus soap and drying the razor, he ran cold water into the bath.

Even with his dressing-gown partially covering him he shivered — it was freezing cold in the room. When the water had risen to three inches he threw off his dressing-gown which he had temporarily thrown round his shoulders, stripped off his nightshirt and stepped into the freezing water. Gasping with the effort he lowered himself into the bath and proceeded to sponge himself all over. For the space of perhaps ten seconds he spluttered, gasped and blew until he knew it would be unwise to remain in the water a moment longer. Scrambling out, he grabbed a large bath towel and dried himself quickly and thoroughly. Dousing the bathroom light he struggled into his dressing-gown picked up his nightshirt and strode back to the bedroom.

The cold water wash, shave and bath routine had taken place ever since Mr. Learner had started up in business some fifteen years ago. He always maintained that a cold bath every morning was jolly good for you. "You should try it yourself", he told friends and neighbours.

Going downstairs he entered the warm kitchen to be greeted by his wife and by an appetizing smell of bacon frying. "Here you are, dear. Your porridge is ready".

Mrs. Learner took the porringer from the range and poured a generus portion of thick porridge into his warmed plate. She knew he hated 'thin watery stuff' as he called it. The porringer was a well-used blackened utensil with two tiers. The bottom pan held the heated water whilst oats mixed with water were heated in the top compartment.

"Thank you, my dear. By jove it's cold this morning, I couldn't get dressed quickly enough after my bath". He took a mouthful of porridge. "This will warm me up for the journey"

Emma returned the porringer to the range and sat down opposite him. She was a pleasant-looking, robust woman (she could never be called pretty) a year or two younger than Edward. She had a good head of hair — thick tawny tresses pulled back away from her face and tied in a bun at the nape of her neck. One of her greatest attributes was her grand sense of humour; her remarkable mimicking and occasional lapse into a Cornish accent delighted the whole family.

Born and brought up in a humble cottage in Falmouth, she had managed to put aside her humble origins and had developed into a lively, lovable person. Mr. Learner loved his wife devotedly. Despite business worries and endeavouring to afford a good education for his youngsters, he knew he was a lucky man to have such a loving wife and good home.

Breakfast finished, he left the kitchen and bounded up the stairs.

Jim and John, bare-footed and still in their night- clothes, waited for him on the landing. He pointed menacingly at John, picked him up, whirled him round and made to throw him over the bannisters. Dropping John he repeated the performance for Jim then chased by two screaming laughing lads, he ran into Ruth's room and gave the still sleeping child a warm loving hug. He was rewarded with two chubby arms clinging to his neck as she woke from a deep sleep.

A final dash to Peter's room found his eldest son already up and dressed. "Goodbye, father. I hope everything goes well at your factory today".

"Thank you, my son, I hope so too". Mr. Learner was accustomed to the serious demeanour of his eldest. He was very fond of Peter but wished he would sometimes be a little bit more affectionate. He gave him a friendly punch on his shoulder, turned and left the room.

Mrs. Learner handed her husband his scarf, gloves and umbrella, then took a well worn grey trilby hat from the hall stand.

"Here's your hat". Looking down at his shoes she exclaimed, "Oh, you've forgotten your spats".

"Damn!"

"Edward — the children are listening".

Two little faces could be seen watching with great interest the goings-on downstairs. Mr. Learner frantically pulled off his gloves and hastily buttoned up a pair of immaculate grey spats over his ankles. Straightening up he grabbed hold of gloves, hat and umbrella. His trilby hat was always a size too small for him; now he jammed it squarely on top of his head, hurriedly pecked at his wife's cheek, rushed out of the house and ran down Linden Avenue. With a final wave to his wife who had followed him to the front gate, he turned into Wembley Hill Road.

Normally it was only a couple of minutes walk to the station. This morning he had to run fast to the paper shop, snatch up his News Chronicle, dash across the road to the station entrance and run down the slope to the platform. He was only just in time; the Marylebone train was at that moment steaming into the station.

Edward had started his journey to work which would take him

away from wife and family for twelve hours — 7 a.m. to 7 p.m. It was a long day, but he was used to it.

Getting About Wembley Hill

I N this chronicle, Wembley Hill has already been described as a peaceful, quiet, countrified little township. Ten minute walk from the edge of the town took you to the centre of Wembley proper. To the north of Wembley Hill was the area known as Wembley Park (a pleasant residential district) whilst North Wembley stood to the north west of King Edward Seventh Park.

The entire area was well served with public transport; in fact each of the 'Wembleys' had its own railway line and station. The station at Wembley Hill was served by the London & North Eastern Railway, which was originally the Great Central Railway. The line was re-named the L.N.E.R. in 1923. It ran from Marylebone Station in North West London to Gerrard Cross, High Wycombe, Princes Risborough and Aylesbury in Buckinghamshire.

There was a fast line and a slow local line with an adequate service for town travellers during peak hours. The station building was very small with a booking office and a parcel's room. It was typical of many other stations in London and its environs at this time. A station master's house stood adjacent to the station building. The station master himself did duty as ticket issuer, ticket collector, porter and general dogsbody.

Adjacent to the 'up' line and to the rear of the station master's house was a shunting area, used mainly by coal traffic. For a small town like Wembley a considerable number of wagons were to be seen and heard moving to and fro over the network of rails. Lying in bed, the Learner children loved to hear the clunk clunk clunk, clatter clatter of the wagons as they were pushed and pulled by the fussy little shunting engines.

During the rush hour in the evenings, another porter would be on duty to collect tickets on the other side of the wooden bridge. This bridge, not to be confused with the main road bridge carrying vehicular traffic, was entirely for the use of foot passengers crossing from the 'down' to the 'up' line. It was quite a substantial affair with criss-cross iron girders fixed to a wooden platform (or walkway) some six feet wide. It slightly resembled Sydney Bridge in miniature.

Many of the local boys and girls including the Learner gang often joined in the 'dare' game of standing on the bridge, squarely over the fast track, and waiting for an express train to approach and pass beneath them. To do so and experience the tremendous roar, the smoke, the steam and the heat of powerful engine as it rushed beneath them only a few feet down, took quite a bit of courage.

The faint hearts who scuttled away when the train was some distance off had to bear the scornful cries of 'cowardy, cowardy, custard'. To some this was too much to bear. They ran home crying at the injustice of their little friends. Amongst the few who would stand their ground was Peter Learner. Gritting his teeth and hanging on to the iron girders for dear life with his eyes tight shut, he emerged from his ordeal with dishevelled hair and face completely covered in soot. The other children admired his bravery but Peter knew he would have to face a far greater ordeal when he got home.

The station as a whole would never have won a prize for Best Kept Station on the L.N.E.R. Although the booking office and platforms were reasonably clean they were distinctly tatty. The covered area of the 'down' platform was quite presentable, but the remainder, right to the far end of the platform, was rutted and broken up in patches. There were a few beds of rather forlorn- looking flowers.

A row of dismal, dirty, metalled advertisements were attached to the railings on both platforms. A picture of a stout ruddy gentleman clinging frantically to an enormous bottle of Bovril on a choppy sea bore the caption: *Prevent that sinking feeling with Bovril.*

One was encouraged to smoke: *Wills Gold Flake Cigarettes.* The small boy holding a bottle of *Daddies Sauce* was saying: *The only sauce I dare give father* and another advertisement recommended you to: *Use Sunlight Soap.*

Despite the undistinguished conditions of buildings and platforms, Wembley Hill Station was beloved of the locals. They would not have had it any other way.

Other forms of public transport in the district as a whole took the shape of tramcars, omnibuses and a few Hackney Carriages (taxis). A short walk from most part of the residential area of Wembley Hill took you to 'The Triangle'. This was a small railed off portion of ground — triangular in shape as the name indicated — containing a few dusty shrubs and bushes and two separate downward flights of steps leading to the public conveniences some ten or fifteen feet below ground.

On the Wembley High Road side of the triangle stood a sign bearing the legend: London Tramways-Tramcars stop here. Every ten or fifteen minutes a bright red double-decker tramcar came groaning and grinding down the hill from the direction of Sudbury. It pulled up with noisy screeching brakes alongside the triangle stop. Most of them were closed in on top but a few were open-top trams.

As an occasional treat the young Learners were allowed to travel to Harlesden via Stonebridge Park on one of these trams. Their final destination would inevitably be Woolworth's 3d and 6d Stores in the High Road. They loved to spend their few pennies of pocket money on things which, in the long run, were of no use to them at all. That didn't matter — the joy was in the spending. However, on one occasion many years later Peter spent half a crown on an Ingersoll watch. It was still going and in perfect order five years later.

When waiting at the Triangle for a tram, they always let two or three closed top trams go by. On arrival of the right tram there was a mad scramble to be first to get 'up top'. The conductor, red-faced with exertion, breathing heavily and with cap pushed back from his forehead, climbed laboriously up the staircase at the rear of the tram shouting "Tickets please".

An alternative form of transport was the bus. A satisfactory service was provided for the public by the London General Omnibus Company — the red GENERALS. The majority of these were motorised vehicles which were built either at the Albion or Thorneycroft motor body works, but they did not have a complete monopoly of transporting the people of Wembley to their various destinations.

It was becoming an increasingly frequent spectacle to see a blue 'Pirate' bus cutting in front of a GENERAL at a crowded bus stop. Their fares were considerably cheaper than the LGOC buses and apparently there was no statutory or constitutional objection to their picking up fares. But the day of the pirate bus was short lived, and they were only transitorily evident on the London scene.

From time to time a Hackney Carriage appeared on the Wembley streets. Bearing the maker's name UNIC or BEARDMORE on the front grill, they attracted considerable attention from the local residents. With their high superstructure, padded black leather upholstery, an open driver's seat and shining brash headlamps, they gleamed and glistened their stately progress through Wembley's thoroughfare.

A fourth method of transport was available, to a limited extent, to those who could afford one — the light two-wheeled hooded one-horse chaise. To the initiated this long-winded description, translated, indicated a cabriolet — 'cab' for short. Although it was quite a common sight to see these conveyances plying for hire in and around Wembley High Road, the likes of the Learner family would rarely, if ever, be likely to have to hire one.

Every one of the Learners liked to walk. Mr. Learner of course, had to use the train to get to work, and Peter and John travelled from Wembley Park to Harrow-on-the-Hill by train to get to school. Otherwise walking to the shops and the park played a major part in the lives of the whole family. They thought nothing of walking to and from their church on Sunday (three times there and three times back) a distance of six miles in all. It was probably very good for them.

Jim Goes Shopping

THE rain had at last stopped but the pavements were still wet and the drains gurgled with fast-rushing water. Although the wind was still keen it did not have last night's ferocity and bite.

Jim was being sent to the shops before going to school. His mum wanted him to go to the dairy for six cracked eggs, explaining that Mrs. Davy sold them off cheaply when they were cracked. Jim was in his first term in a small establishment in Wembley park run by a governess. Previously he and John were both pupils at an infants' school in Wembley High Road on the corner of Berkhamsted Avenue.

John and Peter were now at private schools in Harrow. John at Quainton Hall, a school of about seventy pupils in Hindes Road, and Peter at the much larger Lower School of John Lyon on Harrow Hill. Ruth was still at Wembley House School in the High Road, but moved on to Harrow County School for Girls.

Jim was painstakingly lacing up his boots, but Mrs. Learner was becoming impatient with him.

"Oh do come on, Jim. What a slow coach you are". She handed him a small earthenware basin. "Now that's for the eggs and mind you don't drop them — or the basin".

"Can I get my Magnet this morning, mummy?" Jim asked anxiously. "Mr. Johns gets them on a Friday".

"You won't have time for that now, you and John can get your magazines tomorrow. Oh, and I've just remembered. Run down to

John and James's before you go to the dairy and get me some more sultanas. I only want four ounces and make sure they're the ones at sevenpence-halfpenny a pound".

Boots now at last laced up, Jim put on his outdoor things – a grey flannel shirt with blue tie, grey jacket and a pair of knee-length knickerbockers. He struggled into his warm overcoat, wriggled his hands into a pair of woollen mittens and put on a long scarf.

On his head was the bright red woollen tam-o-shanter type hat with red woollen bobble on top, lovingly knitted by Mrs. Learner in the winter evenings, but worn by Jim under protest.

"Now there's a shilling", she said, pulling the cap further down, "and don't forget to let me have the change".

* * * *

Going down the hill he wished he had his roller skates on. The three youngest Learners all had skates and Jim laughed to himself as he thought about how they held onto all the gates, posts and walls as they gingerly descended Linden Avenue. Turning into the main road he skipped along towards Wembley Hill Dairy, which was on his right hand side, just past Mostyn Avenue. Going past the dairy he waved cheerfully to Mrs. Davy who was cleaning the glass on the shop front door, and called out: "Going to see Mr. Devenish first. I'll get some cracked eggs on my way back". Part skipping and part running on, he passed the next two shops and paused at Mr. Johns' premises. Mr. Johns sold newspapers, sweets, cigarettes and tobacco, but what really attracted Jim to the establishment was the wonderful variety of boys' and girls' magazines.

Jim's sworn favourite was 'The Magnet'. He was never happier than when sitting at the kitchen table reading all about the exploits of Harry Wharton & Co. at Greyfriars School. He and John also perused a 'penny dreadful' in which they followed the amusing goings-on of Grock. This strange name when the individual letters were spelt out read: Gather round our comedy king. They laughed until their sides ached at some of Grock's antics.

John favoured 'The Gem' whilst Ruth who would be thirteen in

May, eagerly scanned the pages of 'Film Weekly'. Peter scorned all magazines and dismissed them as 'tripe'. His favourite was a thriller by Edgar Wallace. He also read avidly the stories of Sir Henry Rider Haggard and G.A. Henty. Jim moved on, passing the local branch of Little Laundries Ltd., where he was always fascinated to see huge bundles of washing stacked on the counter, each bundle enclosed in a bed sheet tied up in a knot by the four corners of the sheet, on to Mantells — one of two grocers in Wembley Hill — and on over the railway bridge. He looked down the lane that ran parallel with the railway line. This was Eccleston Place where one could always be certain to see a couple of mechanics tinkering with clapped out cars and motor- bikes. At this point the shops started on the other side of Wembley Hill Road, which swerved round to the left at the end of this parade and from then on ran parallel with many other shops on the opposite side of Wembley High Road.

Before crossing over Jim waited while a huge brewer's dray, drawn by two magnificent shire horses, passed in front of him. The drayman, dressed in the brewer's livery, winked at Jim and flicked his whip at one of the horse's flanks. It should be said here that young Jim, who was quite a good-looking, well set-up lad, invariably seemed to attract the attention of various members of the public. They seemed to like his bright, cheerful, lively disposition. Jumping up and down and waving to the dray man with boyish enthusiasm, he made sure no trams or buses were coming and crossed the road. A boy on a tradesman's bicycle pulled up and gave Jim a cheeky grin. His bicycle was fitted with a large deep almost square wicker basket in front of the handle-bars; it was very nearly as big as the boy himself. This was Harry, John and James's delivery boy and lad of many parts. He entered the grocer's shop and Jim followed him in.

No one had the faintest idea why the establishment should be called John and James, but presumed it was originally run by two brothers or partners with those particular Christian names. It was solid, spotlessly clean, old fashioned and with an excellent reputation for good quality comestibles and fair prices. Jim, like the majority of customers upon entering the shop, was overwhelmed by the magical, near-oriental atmosphere of spices, sugars, tropical fruits, sacks of corn, sacks of nuts and a huge variety of currants, raisins and sultanas. There was a selection of crystallised fruits that Jim and probably many others had never seen, or heard of, before. It was a shop that he found utterly fascinating. He was equally fascinated by the larger-than-life manager, Mr Devenish, and his assistant Miss Redmayne.

Mr. Devenish was in his mid-fifties, stockily built and invariably immaculately turned out. Every customer was treated with never-failing respect and good humour. Bonhomie positively oozed out of him. His assistant was an extremely tall lady of about forty summers. She was invariably dress in a severe black blouse, nearly-floor-length black crepe skirt and black lace-up calf length boots. She wore not a trace of make-up or jewellery for relief, and her every movement about the shop could only be described as regal. Jim looked round at the shelves where the huge containers of dried fruits were kept. "Can I have four ounces of sultanas please – the ones that cost sevenpence-halfpenny a pound".

"You can, my son. Quarter of best sultanas, replied Mr. Devenish in his distinct Cockney accent.

He handed Jim a quarter pound packet of 'best' sultanas. He liked Mrs. Learner and made sure he gave her the more expensive fruits. "That'll cost yer a penny-halfpenny". Jim handed over the shilling and received tenpence-halfpenny change. "Thank you very much" he said "I'd better hurry now or I'll be late for school. Good-bye, Mr. Devenish", and he hurried towards the door clutching bag of sultanas and basin.

As he opened the door he heard a bell ringing in the distance, and within a few seconds a fire engine came racing past from the direction of the Fire Station in St. Johns Road. The shining red Merry-weather engine with its rickety turntable and complement of half a dozen helmeted firemen, one of whom was ringing the bell with frenzied energy, sped off in the direction of Stonebridge Park.

Cars, carts and buses all stopped or drew into the side of the road to make way for the racing vehicle. Jim's father had told him some time ago that before motorised fire engines were put into service, the local fire engine was horse drawn.

Jim hurried on to the dairy where six large cracked eggs were added to the basin. He handed over sixpence and with a hurried "Thanks Mrs. Davy" ran out.

The Wembley Hill Dairy was on the corner of Mostyn Avenue and Jim was just about to cross over the bottom end of this avenue when he nearly ran into three boys who were pointing at him and laughing loudly as they saw what he was carrying. He knew them from past experience. They were pupils at the council school in Park Lane and the biggest of the three, Jack Thorpe, was, in Jim's view, a bully and a rotter.

"Leave me alone", shouted Jim. He tried to push them off, holding on to the basin for dear life, but he was outnumbered. They all now grabbed hold of the basin, Jack Thorpe knocking it upwards out of Jim's hands. Basin and beautiful brown eggs shot up in the air and landed with a sickening crash on the ground. The packet of sultanas suffered the same fate, the packet burst open and sultanas scattered all over the wet pavement.

A furious and tearful Jim lashed out at his three assailants but they were obviously too much for him. One of the boys snatched Jim's red woollen hat from his head, threw it to the ground and stamped on it. Then all ran off, laughing and jeering, leaving Jim to pick up his filthy muddy hat.

Jim gazed at the ruin of eggs, sultanas and basin on the pavement, gathered up his filthy sodden hat and ran sobbing homewards. Hammering on the front door of Letchworth, he cried bitterly while he waited for his mother to open the door. Mrs. Sanders from No. 27 up the hill was just passing by; she looked curiously at Jim and was about to speak to him when the door was thrown open.

"Mummy, mummy", wailed Jim, "those boys broke all the eggs". He dashed indoors, rushed into the kitchen and sobbed his heart out standing at the table. A horrified Mrs. Learner making a sign of trouble to Mrs. Sanders, closed the door and walked grimly into the kitchen. She seized Jim by the shoulders and spoke very sharply to him: "Now, Jim, stop crying and tell me — which boys were they?"

Anxious Days

FRIDAY evenings in the Learner household were quite different from other week-day evenings. After supper eaten in the kitchen with the whole family present, Mr. Learner always repaired to the dining-room to deal with the weekly accounts.

This particular evening he had come home tired, cold and very hungry. His wife saw he had a strained look about him. She was worried but said nothing as they all took their seats at the kitchen table and tucked into her delicious steak and kidney pie.

Jim was still red-eyed with crying from his experience and glancing at his son Mr. Learner said: "You told me briefly what happened to Jim this morning, mother. I've a good mind to go round and see those boys' parents".

"Can't we do something about those louts, father? They're always making a nuisance of themselves in the district", said Peter. Mr. Learner was about to answer but his wife interrupted.

"Well I've already tried to do something, Peter. After I'd sent Jim off to Mrs. Maxton with a note apologising for him being late, I went round to Mostyn Avenue". She turned to her husband. "I know where that Thorpe family live and I have occasionally spoken to Mrs. Thorpe down in the town".

"I was already to give Mrs. Thorpe a piece of my mind. But I was quite shocked when she came to the door. She'd obviously been crying; her eyes were all red and she looked really dreadful". All the family were looking at her, wondering what was coming. "I started to tell her what I thought about her boy's behaviour when she cried all the more and said something about she couldn't control him and her husband had been knocking her about and she just didn't know what she was going to do".

"Well — it properly took the wind out of my sails so I said I was sorry and started to come away again". Mr. Learner nodded his head in sympathy. "She called out that she would pay for the eggs as I was walking down the garden path, but I said no, it didn't matter".

"Quite right, my dear", agreed her husband. "We can't do any more about it". He turned to his children. "Just try and keep out of the way of that Thorpe boy and his cronies. That's all you can do".

They all nodded in agreement and the meal proceeded.

* * * *

As he entered the dining-room Edward Learner was grateful to observe that a cheerful fire was burning in the grate. He warmed his hands in front of the fire for a few moments before lighting the two gas mantles and one of the candles standing in its holder on the sideboard. The heavy chenille cloth had already been removed from the dining-room table.

He sat at one end of the table which was on hinges. When folded back to its fullest extent, at right angles to the rest of the table, it was held in place by two metal brackets on each side of the table.

The lifting of this end section revealed a horizontal surface for writing, covered with red morrocco leather. There were several racks and pigeon-holes for documents, three bottles of black, green and red inks slotted into grooves on the writing surface and a selection of pens, pencils, rulers and blotting paper all exactly and precisely lodged into their correct positions. The whole thing was beautifully made. It was a work of art and Mr. Learner was justly proud of it.

Before sorting out the bills, statements and invoices which he would be dealing with tonight, he reached over to the sideboard for his heavy glass ashtray and cigarettes. Opening a new packet of twenty Turf cigarettes, he selected one, bent down and lit a 'spill' which he took from an old jam jar in the grate, lit his cigarette, threw the spill into the fire and leant back to enjoy his first after supper smoke.

He had been smoking cigarettes for twenty years, ever since his first attempt to try a 'gasper' when working as an assistant at Swan & Edgar's. In all that time he could not bring himself to inhale. It was a case of puffing away at the start of each cigarette, leaving it to burn on the ashtray or doing whatever he happened to be doing with the cigarette dangling from his lips.

Leafing through the household bills he extracted those for groceries which had been delivered during the week. His wife paid the milkman and the bread man on the doorstep. Half a ton of coal had been delivered on Monday; at four shillings a hundredweight the bill was quite hefty. He turned to two bills for items of clothing supplied to his two youngest boys. A worried frown creased his forehead when he saw the amounts involved.

A new school uniform had been ordered for Jim when he started his education at the Maxton's house in Wembley Park. This was a beautiful old house in Oakington Avenue, run by a governess by the name of Miss Henderson. There were only four pupils, three boys and one girl, although another little girl was due to join the class shortly. The two other boys were wearing smart school uniforms and caps when Tom started his first term there and Mrs. Learner was not going to allow Jim to be ashamed at having to wear his ordinary clothes to school.

That was one item. The other was a bill for a new winter overcoat for John; he was growing up fast. Mr. Learner knew that John's old overcoat was both too small and too tight. One consolation was that it could be handed on to Jim for playing in the garden etc. His worry increased when he remembered that Ruth was starting at her new school next term, and that meant an entirely new outfit.

He got up to put more coal on the fire. There was a tap on the door. John and Jim rushed in to say good-night, and as they ran off Mrs. Learner came in holding a cup of tea for her husband.

"Is everything all right, dear?" she asked, turning one of the vacant chairs towards the fire. "I thought you looked a bit strained when you came home". She sat slowly without taking her eyes off his face. Mr. Learner took another sip of his tea. He put the cup and saucer on the table and shook his head.

"No, Emma, everything's not all right. It looks to me as if we're all going to have to tighten our belts a bit. We're spending more on our day to day living than I've got money coming in from the business". Emma stared at him lovingly but did not interrupt.

"I've just been going through some of the bills which have got to be paid shortly. They're quite steep: John's new overcoat, for example, and next term I've got to fork out a considerable amount of money on Ruth's new school uniform. We're only six weeks away from Christmas and you know what that means?

"I wanted to keep it from you, my dear, but it's only fair that you should know". Emma's comely face was creased with anxiety.

"You remember I told you a few weeks ago that I'd received a large order from St. Columb's Hospital". Emma nodded. "It was for a hundred nurses' uniforms, forty or fifty sisters' uniforms and twenty housecoats for the hospital doctors".

"Yes of course I remember, dear. You said it was one of the largest orders you'd received in many years and I said I was so very happy about it. Why, isn't the order going well?" Edward shook his head.

"I'm very annoyed about it. Originally I was told that the order should be executed as soon as possible. Well – I put in an order for several bales of white cotton drill and that was exactly three weeks ago today. And now this morning I received a letter from the hospital administrator advising me that the complete order must be ready for despatch by the middle of December. That's only three weeks away".

He looked despairingly at his wife. "It's an absolute impossibility with the small staff I've got. I've written off this morning asking for more time. Depending on their reply, if they say the middle of December must be adhered to I shall have to turn away the order. And, I would have the problem of several bales of cotton surplus to my requirements. I think it's most unfair of the hospital – and I've been dealing with them for a very long time – to insist on such short notice".

Emma stood up and put her arms round his neck. "I think it's terribly unfair, Edward, dear. We can only hope and pray that they will try and be a bit more reasonable with you. In the meantime, as you say we'll just have to be careful with our expenditure".

Edward stubbed out his cigarette in the ashtray. He picked up his packet of Turf cigarettes and showed it to Emma. "That's one thing I'm going to cut down on. I smoke too much, anyway, and I shall try not to smoke at all at the factory".

"And I shall give up my occasional glass of milk stout", Emma said.

Her husband nipped that in the bud right away. "That's not necessary, dear. And in any case Doctor Dyson told you it would do you good from a health point of view to drink stout whenever you felt it necessary".

Emma hugged him and kissed the top of his head. Edward smiled at her and went on ruefully: "But I'm afraid there's one thing I shall be forced to postpone for the forseeable future. And this is the worst part.

"I was about to take out life insurances policies for all the children, but as things stand at the moment I won't be able to find the money for the initial premiums". He bent forward and looked pensively into the fire. "The last thing I wanted was to deprive my dear children of an adequate insurance to help them when they start out in the world".

Emma knew that any words would be superfluous. She sat gently on his knee and together they stared at the flames burning brightly in the grate. Each of them pondered on the seriousness of the situation. They prayed that with God's help they would survive the uncertainties and anxieties of the days and weeks to come.

A Mystery Parcel

AS long as the children could remember Saturday afternoon was by custom devoted to 'doing the circulars'. The entire family congregated in the dining room where father wrote the circulars. The children, sitting round the table with him, folded them up and put them into envelopes.

The weather was still distinctly chilly and a welcome fire roared in the grate. At other times when the circulars were not being dealt with, Jim and John would take it in turns to place chestnuts on the top bar of the grate.

On this Saturday afternoon Mrs. Learner was seated by the window doing embroidery. She was making a cushion cover for the church bazaar at Christmas. It was getting dark and she knew the lamp and gas mantles would soon have to be lit. The circulars, as Mr. Learner liked to call them, were printed illustrations of the clothing made in his factory in the City. They were printed in a peculiar reddish brownish colour with a heading showing the following legend:-

EDWARD J. LEARNER,
47a, OLD STREET, LONDON EC.1.
TELEPHONE NO. CLERKENWELL 2951.
OVERALL MANUFACTURERS.
BOILER SUITS • DENIMS
BIB-AND-BRACE SETS • ALPACA JACKETS
NURSES' & DOCTORS COATS • DUNGAREES
All orders dealt with efficiently and promptly.

Half a dozen drawings of male and female models, wearing a selection of the type of protective clothing manufactured, were set out under the circular heading.

Mr. Learner had been able to set up his own business after scraping together sufficient capital. He had found suitable premises in the City and by 1920 was well established in his Old Street factory. Until the recent setback with the hospital order, he had accumulated a quite respectable profit. He was well-known and respected in the vicinity for his reliability in executing orders to the satisfaction of all his customers.

These orders were obtained in the main by sending off weekly circulars to known and potential customers whose names appeared in the London Telephone Directory. In 1920 this directory which covered the entire London Postal area, was just three-quarters of an inch thick!

On two evenings a week, when the children had been packed off to bed, Mr. Learner sat with the directory open in front of him, the inevitable cigarette in his mouth. Pen in hand, he would laboriously scan the alphabetical index for businesses which would be likely to need overalls of any description for their employees. He ticked off their names and painstakingly wrote them and their addresses in the blank panel at the bottom of each circular.

When folded correctly the circulars fitted exactly into window envelopes. The flaps were turned in allowing a halfpenny stamp to be used for postage purposes. Any other type of letter posted required a penny stamp.

The Learner children were dutifully engaged in folding, inserting and stamping the completed circulars. Jim and John were really too young to understand why they were doing this exercise, but it was the intention of their father to take each of his children, in due course, to the City with him.

The idea was to show them where his factory was situated and to see for themselves how the overalls etc. were turned out. In this way the need for the circulars would become evident to them all. In fact Peter had been promised that his turn would be next Saturday morning.

Mrs. Learner, as she glanced up occasionally from her embroidery, never failed to be amused and proud to watch the expressions of each child as he or she dealt with a circular. Jim invariably had his mouth open and his tongue darted out to lick his lips with extreme concentration. He wanted to ensure his circulars were correctly folded and inserted.

John had the habit of humming a tune (and frequently not in tune) to the intense annoyance of Peter. Ruth was for ever tossing back her long dark hair which would keep falling forward and so impeding her progress. Peter's face was usually quite impassive and controlled. He would show the others how simple it was to help his father in the best possible way.

This practice continued for about an hour and a half by which time the two youngest became restive. Jim's concentration flagged. His eyes wandered to the bookcase on one shelf of which were eight volumes of Harmsworth's Encyclopaedia. They were a great favourite with all the children, not so much for the information they contained but because of the interesting little sketches explaining many of the words used.

Eventually the table was laid for tea, the muffins were brought in and the well-worn toasting fork was removed from its hook at the side of the grate. Whilst the children took it in turns to toast the muffins, mother brought in an enormous 'cut and come again' cake. The sheer delight of the currants, sultanas, peel, 'goodness' and other ingredients with which it was packed ensured that few could resist another slice. Hence the name.

Try as they would the children could never get their mother to explain exactly what 'goodness' was. "Well, it's quite simple, my dears", she blandly explained, "all you do is mix a few ounces of goodness with the rest of the ingredients". They had to be satisfied with that explanation.

When tea was well under way Peter asked: "Why are we having tea in the dining-room, mother? We always have it in the kitchen".

Mrs. Learner glanced at her husband and smiled when she saw the excitement in his eyes. "Your father's got a surprise for you".

Peter looked at his father. "I saw you had a parcel with you, father, when you came home last night. A big square box. I bet that's what the surprise will be. Am I right?"

Mr. Learner wiped his mouth on his serviette, took a last sip of tea and looked round the table to see if everyone had finished. "Now then, children, clear the table, help mother with the washing-up, and when you've finished all come back in together. Then you'll see what the surprise is".

* * * *

There followed a frenzied scramble to get everything out into the scullery in record time. Mr. Learner smiled to himself as he listened to the excited chatter coming from the back of the house. He went to the sideboard and, reaching right to the back of it, withdrew a brown paper parcel.

The heavy chenille table-cloth was now divested of all traces of the tea things. He placed the parcel on it and took out a penknife which he always carried in the left pocket of his trousers. The parcel was approximately 12 inches square and was tied with strong white twine. He cut the twine and carefully unfolded the brown paper wrapping. The object which was revealed was placed in the middle of the dining-room table. There was an excited scramble along the hallway before the dining-room door burst open. The children gathered round the table and stared, eyes open wide, at the object on the table. Mrs. Learner followed them in, closed the door quietly and stood by her husband.

A whole host of questions, some ridiculous and some a bit more sensible, followed in quick succession. Mr. Learner waited for the hubbub to cease. He held up his hand for quiet and leant over the table to remove the top of the box. It was padded with dark green leather. Placing the top on the table beside the box he watched with amusement as four heads gawped at the contents.

He now moved close to the box and carefully removed the strangest-looking object the children had ever seen in their lives. There were two tiny pieces of 'glass' attached to two metal rods set into small blocks of wood. Each one was set on either side of the interior of the box. Protruding from the bits of 'glass' were extremely fine half-inch lengths of wire. The whole of this contraption was firmly attached to a wooden base.

Watched with complete absorption, Mr. Learner lifted the contraption out of the box revealing further mysteries in its lower part. He placed the top portion very carefully on the table. Finally he lifted out a two foot coil of wire attached to an extraordinary object consisting of a metal headband with ear- pieces fixed to each end of the headband. These he also placed on the table. The children were now almost beside themselves with curiosity, all four vying with each other in the questioning of their father.

"What's it for? What do you do with it?"

"Is it a musical instrument of some sort, daddy?"

"What are those funny little bits of glass for?"

"I believe all these things are joined together in some way, aren't they father?" This last query from Peter.

"Well, children, I can see you're all bursting with curiosity. Peter is quite right. They do all get joined together and they make (pausing for effect) a crystal set!"

He uncoiled the wire which was separate from the wire attached to the headband. One end of this much longer piece of wire he attached to an aperture in the crystal set. The other end he attached to a picture hook high up on the picture rail. Next he straightened out the wire fixed to the headband. The end of this wire he plugged in to another aperture in the set.

"Now you've got to be absolutely quiet while I experiment with these two fine wires on the set".

He took out his half-hunter watch, glanced at it, nodded and replaced the watch in his waistcoat pocket. He pulled his chair right up to the table and concentrated on the delicate operation in hand. All four children and their mother, equally excited as each other, watched with fascination as he manoeuvred the two ends of the wires into precisely the right position.

At last he made an exclamation. He nodded to himself in obvious satisfaction. A further confirmation of his evident success was shown by the removal of the headphones. "Right. Now, whatever you do don't touch the set and don't jog the table.

He looked round at all of them. He was met with expressions of such agonised suspense that he couldn't suppress a loud laugh. "All right, now I'm going to start with Peter and then you can each one in turn put on these headphones. Yes, these are called headphones". He handed them to a somewhat apprehensive Peter who had no idea why he should be putting on such a strange looking contraption. His father helped him to settle them correctly on his head. Immediately Peter looked up with an expression which could only be described as wide-eyed astonishment.

"There's someone talking. I can hear a voice! It sounds like a man but I can't be sure; it's not very clear and there's a lot of noise in the background". He glanced up at his father. The other three were goggle-eyed with curiosity.

He motioned to Peter to take off the headphones who handed them reluctantly to Ruth. After a few minutes of unbelieving astonishment at what she was hearing, she in turn was persuaded to hand them on to John. Jim was becoming frantic to know what all this tremendous excitement was about. He in turn was equally astonished at the sounds emanating from the headphones.

When Jim had finally been persuaded to take off the headphones, Mr. Learner carefully lifted the wonder contraption and carried it to the end of the table. He settled himself in his own chair and began to explain, as well as he could, to a very young audience, how a crystal set worked.

"There is a building somewhere in London where they have a transmitting machine, which sends out signals. In some extraordinary way they are put out into the air, relayed and end up on this crystal set.

"Then when they arrive at Letchworth the signals travel down this wire which I believe is called an aerial". He pointed to the wire positioned on the picture rail; his finger followed the wire until it terminated on the crystal set.

"Now this signal is forced on to this little bit of glass. The little bit of glass is called a loadstone or iron pyrite and inside the load-stone are tiny fragments of crystal. Thus the name crystal set. And on the ends of the two loadstones are these very fine magnetic wires which look to me just like cats' whiskers".

"Why did you look at your watch before you started to try and get the two wires together, father?" asked Peter.

"A good question, my son. A friend in the City told me these signals, or voices, are only sent out at certain times of the day. We were lucky that we could try out the crystal set just at the right time this evening".

With all the struggling going on between the four of them to keep the headphones to themselves, it was inevitable that the table was jogged and the signal was lost. This was the 'signal' for mother to step in.

"All right, now, that's enough. You can listen to the voices again tomorrow". Protests from all sides. But mother was adamant. "Now you heard what I said; you can go upstairs and have a wash and clean your teeth. Put your dressing-gowns on and when I call you, you can all come down again and go into the withdrawing- room. Your father's going to play a few pieces on the piano. I know how much you like that".

Mr. Learner was packing up the various bits of the crystal set. "Just before you run upstairs, look at what I'm doing with the set. You see, headphones and wires right at the bottom of the box, this piece of wood on top of that and the set itself resting on the piece of wood, and so it all packs neatly into the box. Then when I replace the lid, like so, it will be put down there at the side of the grate and whoever is roasting chestnuts can sit on the box holding the toasting fork. And no touching the contents of the box. Now off you go upstairs".

The children raced out of the room. When the door closed behind them Edward and Emma stood quietly by the fire gazing at the flames. They loved their children devotedly but they were always glad of a few moments of peace and quiet. Four sturdy growing youngsters gave them very little chance of such a luxury.

The Family at Worship

SUNDAY morning dawned crisply bright and dry. After break-fast with the washing-up tackled and thankfully completed, all thoughts turned to preparations for going to church. Half a dozen pairs of assorted boots and shoes were lined up outside the coal shed to be energetically brushed and polished by two of the children whose turn it was.

Mother told each of her boys that his suit must be brushed and clean, his socks must be properly held up with elastic garters and his tie must have a decent knot in it. In Peter's case, as he was the only boy to be wearing long trousers, he should be sure to wear a pair with a good crease in them.

Ruth, however, was the problem. Never one to care much about her appearance, she was just as likely to try and get away with an old school skirt and black stockings. But mother would have none of it. Her protesting daughter was sent back upstairs and told to change into a suitable dress and decent stockings. When she came down again she looked quite presentable with a piece of white rib-bon bound round her hair.

There had been a bit of trouble with John. Father had caught him taking the lid off the crystal set box. Despite strong protests that he was 'only peeping' he was banned from touching the set for the rest of the day. Strong parental control was essential.

Shortly before they had all assembled in the hall for a dress in-spection, mother could be heard in the kitchen damping down the range boiler. A delicious mouth-watering aroma wafted into the hall. A huge cooking pot containing beef stew was slowly simmering on top of the range. Mrs. Learner always tried on a Sunday morning to have the dinner made ready as far as possible before they set out for church.

Father came downstairs dressed in his Sunday best. There was no doubt he could be described as sartorially elegant. Starting from the top he sported his cherished grey trilby hat with an immaculately curled brim. Like all his other hats it was too small for him and sat precariously perched on top of his head. A high-winged starched collar was complemented by a smart grey cravat, graced at the centre with a pearl pin. Under his overcoat he wore a well-cut dark grey three piece suit. The overcoat was fashioned out of excellent quality slightly grey worsted, and in the manner of the day's accepted fashion, was slimly cut and reached down to the level of the calves. A pair of grey spats with gloves to match finished off a remarkably smart ensemble.

Mrs. Learner was more modestly dressed in a long black coat which reached down to her ankles, and a feathered stole. Her hat which was her pride and joy, was a black straw arrangement which fitted well down on her head and was only stopped from dropping further down by several fearsome-looking ebony-ended hatpins. It was colourfully surrounded with intermingled cherries, small chinaware flowers, multi-coloured beads and other gew-gaws. Sensible shoes and gloves completed her outfit.

All in all it was a well-turned out, happy, God-fearing family unit assembled in the hallway waiting to start the walk to church. But they could not go yet. Mr. Learner noticed that the knot of Peter's tie was not exactly positioned between the two points of his collar. A brief adjustment followed. Then with a final look round at his patiently-waiting offspring he opened the front door.

* * * *

Edward and Emma Learner were devout worshippers. Edward was descended from parents who were themselves strict practising churchgoers. Emma was brought up in a community in Cornwall where attending church services was as natural as breathing. It fol-

51

lowed that their children were regular attenders at their chosen church.

Peter was very happy about going to church, he enjoyed the hymn singing, but was honest enough to admit to his parents that he found the sermons much too long. The other three went because it was expected of them. Every Sunday, regardless of the vagaries of the weather, they trudged along behind the rest of the family on the mile-long walk to St. Andrew's Church in Ealing Road.

Every Sunday afternoon, whether they felt like it or not, they repeated the walk there and back in order to attend Sunday School in the church hall. Mercifully they were spared the misery of a third walk to the same destination on Sunday evenings. Edward invariably attended Sunday evening services, sometimes with his wife. Emma always had the excuse, on the occasions when she did not accompany her dearly beloved, that she was not happy about leaving the children on their own. This practice of regularly attending church services came about because they genuinely loved their Lord. They had so much to thank Him for.

But it must be said that quite a sizeable proportion of the population went to church because in this period immediately after the war there was little else to do. Television was unknown. The wireless set was in its embryonic infancy. The only cinema in Wembley did not open its doors on the Sabbath. Few people patronised the one and only public house in the vicinity of Wembley.

In 1922 the population of Wembley Central was approximately 16,000. For the religious needs of the community there was a wealth of churches of many different denominations. The Learners worshipped at the Presbyterian Church. The Church Hall, where Jim and John went to for their cubs and Scouts meetings, was built in 1902. The adjoining church was dedicated for worship on November 29, 1904. At the time these two buildings were being erected, Ealing Road was named Watery Lane. This nomenclature was given because of the frequent flooding of the stream flowing in a dip in Ealing Road.

The Parish Church, known as St. John's, was finally completed in 1859 when the North Aisle was added to the building. The vicar, the

Reverend J.W.P. Silvester, was inducted in 1896. He continued to serve the church in this capacity until 1944. In later years his son, Victor, achieved fame by becoming a well-known and greatly respected dance band leader.

The Methodists worshipped in a smallish, somewhat mean building on the corner of Park Lane and Wembley High Road. In due course this was demolished and a handsome building was erected on the same site. It became a well-known, much-loved and distinctive landmark to the people of Wembley.

The fourth place of worship was the Roman Catholic Church, St. Joseph's. Situated in Wembley High Road and opposite the triangle, it stood next to Dr. Dyson's surgery. It was Dr. Dyson who helped to bring every Learner child into the world.

So, spiritually speaking, the inhabitants of Wembley Central were well provided for. Within a tram or a bus ride of the town centre four other places of worship opened their doors to seekers of salvation. St. James', Alperton, was within half a mile of the Presbyterian Church, being situated at opposite ends of Ealing Road. St. Augustine's in Wembley Park was easily accessible to residents in the Wembley Hill area; say about a twenty-minute walk. This was the church whose fabric was built entirely of corrugated iron. Inevitably it gained the irreverent title of Tin Tab! At diametrically opposite ends of Wembley Town could be found the church of St. Andrew's at Sudbury and St. Michael's at Tokyngton. Eight churches within a circumference of two and a half to three miles.

It was true to say that almost without exception all of these Houses of God were well filled every Sunday by the good people of Wembley and its environs. St. Andrew's Presbyterian Church in Ealing Road, the one frequented by the Learner family, was certainly no exception.

* * * *

Outside Letchworth the family deliberated on which route to take to church. Normally father decided that they would go up or down hill. Today, however, he left it to the children to decide.

If the final decision was uphill this meant quite a steep climb to the top of the avenue. However the climb would be rewarded by a lovely view of King Edward the Seventh's Park. A walk down the narrow pathway skirting Dagmar House — a mad scramble as far as the children were concerned — would take them to Park Lane. Then a walk along Park Lane, about a quarter of a mile, would take them to the junction of the High Road. From there it was nearly half-a-mile to the church.

If the decision was downhill the route was more interesting to the children because of the presence of buses, trams and horse-drawn vehicles. On Sunday the decision on which route to take led to a heated quarrel between Peter and Ruth.

"I want to go up the hill", pleaded Ruth, "Mummy, I saw those three kittens outside Mrs. Farmer's house. Oh, daddy, can we have one of those darling kittens, please?"

Peter spoke quite crossly to his sister. "Don't start all that again, sis. Father's told us we're not having a kitten, so that's that".

His tone infuriated Ruth, "Who do you think you are, talking to me like that? You great big silly".

Father's tone was firm. "If you can't agree amongst yourselves, your mother and I are taking the downhill route and that's the way we're all going. And if we don't hurry we'll be late for church". They all knew this was quite incorrect, but nobody would say so. It was a well-known fact that Mr. Learner insisted on getting to church at least a quarter of an hour before the service started.

He strode firmly down the hill towards Wembley Hill Road, his wife holding his arm and the four children, in varying degrees of temper, tagging along behind. They proceeded towards the triangle on a road practically empty of traffic or pedestrians. Wembley Hill Road was fairly quiet even on a weekday; on Sunday's vehicular traffic was conspicuous by its absence.

They crossed the road at the junction with the High Road and passing St. Joseph's Roman Catholic Church and Dr. Dyson's surgery, approached Wembley House School. Ruth was still a pupil here, but would be starting at Harrow County School next summer.

Boys and girls were educated at this well-run secondary school. Miss Skinner was the headmistress of the girls' section. Headmaster of the boys' school was Mr. F.S. Skinner. The house itself was a very pleasant rambling old building with ample playground facilities for both sexes.

The Learners had gone only a few steps beyond the school when a No. 18 bus trundled past them. It was on its way to Sudbury and Wealdstone. This particular route harked back to the era of horse-drawn buses. The family would have been extremely surprised if they could have known that the No. 18 bus route, some 60 years ahead, would still be traversing the identical route.

They continued up the slight rise in the road before going downhill for fifty yards or so to the junction with Park Lane. It was here that John, hearing the unmistakable clip-clop of a horse's hooves excitedly exclaimed that Daisy was coming. They all looked round as the strange-looking combination of pony, trap and passenger caught up with them. The children waved merrily as Mr. Ecclestone smilingly inclined his head towards them, Mr. Learner raised his hat and his wife nodded graciously towards the seated figure.

Mr. Ecclestone and his wife Anne were noted celebrities in the district. She was a charming lady who devoted a great deal of her time and money in supporting local good works and charities. Her husband was a huge man with a reputation of being a one-time formidable heavyweight boxer. He was affectionatly called Jolly Jumbo. Because of his tremendous weight his trap was weighted in the opposite seat as compensation for his colossal bulk! The turning off Wembley Hill Road known as Ecclestone Place had been named after his wife.

As the pony and trap continued its ponderous journey, the Learner family had now covered well over half the distance of the walk to church. Mother was looking over the road at Blands, one of Wembley's drapers' shops. She told her husband how she had seen exactly what she wanted in the shop last week. Her lace curtains in the withdrawing room were now distinctly shabby and the ones in Blands were only ninepence three-farthings a yard. But, of course, she knew that in the present circumstances the curtains would have to wait. She was rewarded with a loving sympathetic squeeze on her arm from Edward.

Approaching Wembley Town Station they were all amused to see a very old, very shaky Trojan coming towards them on the opposite side of the road. The Trojans were fairly solid box-like upright family cars with a reputation of good mechanical reliability. But their one drawback was the fact that they were fitted with solid rubber tyres, which were quite narrow. In thoroughfares which had tramlines set in them, the Trojans were apt to get stuck in the track, and this was exactly what happened to the one seen by the Learners.

The car pulled out on to the crown of the road so that it could avoid a cyclist travelling in the same direction. Ruth, Jim and John – and even Peter – hooted with laughter as they watched the driver struggle desperately to extricate his wheels from the tramlines. After twenty or thirty yards of frantic wrestling with the steering wheel the car emerged from its 'anchorage'.

There then followed a small discussion as to whether they should go down to the steps leading to Station Grove or carry on along the High Road. The steps were narrow and steep. They led into a quiet, ancient area of very old houses and one or two shops. It was said that Station Grove and Montrose Crescent had remained unaltered for over a hundred years.

Mr. Learner ruled that this morning they would take the main road route to church, now only two or three hundred yards distant. Reaching the corner of Ealing Road they could look across the High Road and see Killip's drapery establishment, standing on the corner of Lancelot Road.

Killip's was the favourite haunt of Mrs. Learner. It was within those portals that she would have liked to buy so many things for the home. The children, too, loved entering this Aladdin's cave of materials, dress fabrics, buttons, bed-linen, haberdashery and a wonderful assortment of everything imaginable in the drapery line. The shop had an all pervading atmosphere of cosy intimacy. But – and this was a big but – it was the cash carrier which fascinated them above all else.

The whole of the shop area was festooned with wires leading from every counter to a large office set high up in the corner of the emporium. The counter assistant, on completion of a sale, placed the customer's money and the bill in a metal cup, which was screwed on to the top half of the container. This resembled an inverted cup, When a handle was pulled the entire assembled container shot along on the wire and landed with a loud clunk in a metal basket in the cashier's office.

In a few moments the operation was reversed. The container whizzed back to the assistant and the change and receipt were handed to the customer. It was vastly exciting to the children especially when the shop was really busy. Then, containers were whizzing about all over the place in rich confusion. Killip's was the only shop in Wembley to have this remarkable contraption.

No doubt these thoughts were going through the young Learner's minds as they walked the few remaining steps down Ealing Road. They turned into the drive in front of the church and entered the portals of St. Andrew's Presbyterian Church.

* * * *

Built in 1904, it was a handsome structure fashioned mainly out of red bricks which had matured with time into a delicate pinkish hue. The brickwork rose to a height of about seven feet all round the circumference of the building. Frosted glass windows were set above the brickwork along the two sides of the church diffusing a reasonable amount of daylight to the assembled worshippers. The design of the building was unusual in that it was dome-shaped at one end.

Three sections of pews, two end sections and one wide section in the middle, were painted a restful shade of green. A handsome font stood at the top of the steps. Two rows of choir stalls with the organ, console and pipes set in the far corner of the church completed the interior fittings.

The church clock with its distinctive chimes was a feature of St. Andrew's. Every quarter of an hour a solitary 'ding-dong' rang out. On the hour the appropriate number of single chimes could be heard by all and sundry. These chimes, ringing out over the rooftops of Wembley, were all too familiar to the populace. Within the church the muffled sounds of the chimes were heard with mixed feelings by members of the congregation. To the Learner children the chimes meant that the interminable sermon was hopefully coming to an end.

The minister of the church, who was ordained in 1908, was admired and respected by his flock. An Irishman, he had a kindly disposition and was extremely erudite. Shortish and stockily built he must have possessed remarkable staying powers for his sermons frequently lasted well over half an hour. With clear diction he had a habit of emphasising a point with a forceful 'That's it. That's it'.

Jim and John sat through the seemingly endless sermon in a state of utter boredom. They wriggled on the hard seats, sighed noisily and turned round from time to time to peer at people sitting in the pews behind. And the seats were hard. Only a handful of worshippers could afford carpet strips on their pews. Ruth spent sermon time reading through her hymn book. Peter tried to look interested but even he couldn't help stifling a yawn now and then. Yet another 'ding-dong' or the minister's 'and finally' was a sign for them to hope the worst was over.

The congregation stirred thankfully as the minister, with a final and categorical 'that's it', brought the sermon to a close. The organist opened his eyes with a start; he sat in the back seat of the choir stalls, and could clearly be seen nodding off by members of the congregation.

The church caretaker, Mr. Shepherd, ran up the steps from his seat in the front pew and took his stand by the side of the organ behind a green curtain. Among a profusion of other duties his was the responsibility of blowing the church organ at appropriate times.

An electrically-blown organ was unheard of in 1922. It was hand-blown and if the hymns were lengthy it was quite hard work keeping the handle going up and down. On the rare occasions when the caretaker was unavailable for this duty, a senior boy from the Sunday School took over for this quite tiring operation.

On this Sunday morning the final hymn was familiar to one and all. The younger members, greatly relieved that all was nearly over, sang lustily if not always tunefully. Mrs. Learner insisted that as far as possible John and Jim should be seated separately from one another during the service. She was horrified and embarrassed on one occasion when this edict had been overlooked. Looking across at them during the singing of a hymn she saw they were giggling uncontrollably. They were substituting the words 'fishpaste' and 'bananas' for the right and proper words in the hymnbook, and were severely taken to task when they got home.

The last hymn finished and Benediction intoned, the Learners left their seats and mingled with the other worshippers. It was extraordinary the way in which polite greetings were exchanged in church on a Sunday. At other times during the week remarks about certain people's behaviour were not always quite so polite! The minister waited at the porch door to shake hands and have a word with his departing flock. He complained every week to his dear wife that his mangled hand would never be the same again!

Starting the long walk back home, the thoughts of four young healthy children centred upon the mouth-watering beef stew awaiting them at home, and whether they would be allowed to play with that exciting new crystal set.

Some Exciting News

SUNDAY dinner was well under way. The kitchen table was always pulled away from the wall for this meal and in a cosy atmosphere the Learners were tucking into heaped platefuls of that delicious beef stew and dumplings, peas, green beans and mashed potatoes which had been laced with butter and milk.

"Now, leave room, all of you, for your second course". Mother beamed fondly round at her brood. The two youngest wriggled happily in their seats as they hurried to finish off the meat course.

"And don't worry if there's some stew left in the pot". She glanced at her husband. "Have you had enough, daddy?"

Mr. Learner blew out his cheeks in appreciation. "More than enough, my dear. I'm afraid my eyes are bigger than my stomach".

"Oh, that's usually Peter's trouble", she said, glancing at her eldest. Peter was too busy eating to react to her remark. "So, in that case, we'll use what's left for a nibs dinner tomorrow".

'Nibs' were left-overs from a previous meal and were probably peculiar to the Learner family. Although it was never clear where the term 'nibs' originated, it was suspected that the word was, in fact, Cornish in origin. Mrs. Learner was born and brought up in Falmouth. Peter who was clever with the manipulation of words, phrases and spellings in the English language said he was sure the initials stood for: Nice In Between Snacks.

Sometimes a fair amount of meat, for example, was served cold the next day with hot vegetables. All the children loved a nibs meal. Jim, in particular, was a great one for lashings of gravy on his nibs meat. And there was nothing he liked better than lots of hot thick custard on warmed-up nibs apple pie. The parents were always so thankful their children had such tremendous appetites.

As the blackberry and apple pie was brought to the table, Mr. Learner cleared his throat. "Well, children, we're only a few weeks away from Christmas, as you know. I'm sure you'll be happy to know your Aunt Peggy is coming to stay with us over the Christmas holidays".

This announcement started an absolute bedlam of excited cries from all sides. The children simply adored Aunt Peggy.

"Can we all go shopping with her and have rides on the tram and take her into the park?" All this said with breathless excitement by young Jim. Even Peter forgot his dignity. Shouting over the tops of the others he asked: "Could she play French cricket in the garden with us?"

Aunt Peggy was Mr. Learner's youngest sister. He had several brothers and sisters, all of them lively and intelligent, but the youngest one was undoubtedly the brightest spark of them all. A bit of a tomboy, she was always enormously popular with the Learner tribe. On previous visits to Wembley Hill she delighted all the children with the harmless, youthful pranks she played on some of the poor unsuspecting neighburs. Sworn to secrecy they were made to promise that mummy and daddy should not be told of their exploits. Aunt Peggy was always assured of a warm welcome at Letchworth.

When the excitement had abated Mr. Learner spoke again: "All-right, quiet now and listen. You heard Mr. Blakey saying in church this morning that there would be no Sunday School this afternoon..."

"Yes", interrupted his wife, "I was sorry to hear about Mr. Corbett and Mrs. Wimborne. Apparently they've both got influenza".

With the heartlessness of youth John said to Jim in an aside: "If they're both away for a week or two we'll have hours and hours longer to play with our crystal set". Jim grinned and said aloud: "May we play with the crystal set this afternoon, please mummy?"

"No, dear, after dinner you're all going for a long walk down Raglan Gardens". Jim's grin disappeared and was replaced with a look of mock disappointment.

"And if it doesn't rain we shall go as far as Aeroplane Road", Mr. Learner put in. "So, when the washing up's done we'll be on our way".

The announcement was received with mixed feelings. Ruth did not like long walks, preferring to be up in her own bedroom reading the next episode of the serial in Girls' Own Paper. Jim and John normally liked playing with their Meccano sets or making pencil impressions of pictures in the Encyclopedia. Now of course they could think of nothing but their new toy — the crystal set. But even that had been forbidden them this afternoon.

Peter quite liked walking. With his long legs he looked forward to striding along at his father's side. Mrs. Learner was frequently very tired especially at week-ends. The walk to church tired her and when the cooking and serving of the Sunday meal was completed, she felt quite ready for a doze in front of the kitchen range. Her husband would never let her wash the dishes after week-end meals and took charge of the proceedings in the scullery.

Making sure his wife was comfortably seated in front of the range with her feet up, he placed a nice cup of tea near to hand, before supervising the washing up. In no time at all everything was spick and span, and within twenty minutes of finishing the mid-day dinner they were all ready and lined up for the Sunday afternoon walk. For reasons best known to himself Mr. Learner had foregone his favourite after-dinner cigarette.

A Walk Down Raglan Gardens

IN 1921 Wembley Borough Council had proposed grandiose schemes for residential development in the area of Wembley Park Drive. They formulated plans to build an estate of high class homes in Wembley Park Drive itself, Magpie Avenue (later renamed Beechcroft Gardens), Oakington Avenue and Raglan Gardens (formerly The Avenue).

A few of these properties in Oakington Avenue and Wembley Park Drive had already been built when the government stepped in and announced that a halt was to be called to all further constructions. Although secrecy surrounded the reason for this decision, it soon became known that plans were afoot to site the British Empire Exhibition in Wembley Park. This meant that for the time being no new houses would be built in Raglan Gardens. Mr. Learner had a good idea of what was going on from what he read in the papers. The children were blissfully unaware of the extent of the development hanging over their heads.

So the Learners were free to continue strolls along their favourite route. With Mr. Learner and Peter setting the pace they all started down Linden Avenue.

Passing the derelict area at the foot of the hill they saw the old tramp had returned from one of his wanderings. He spent a lot of his time sleeping in a ramshackle old hut left by a former allotment

63

holder. On his travels he was a familiar sight to the locals dressed in awful old rags and muttering to himself as he stumbled along. Although he sometimes frightened the children he was perfectly harmless.

They turned left into Wembley Hill Road, passed the few shops on the left hand side and soon came to the junction with Raglan Gardens. This winding country lane was about half a mile long and joined Wembley Park Drive at the distant end. The weather had turned much colder again and they were all glad of warm overcoats, woolly scarves and fur lined gloves. Jim and John ran on ahead as soon as they had rounded the bend in Raglan Gardens, racing each other to get to the fence first.

This wooden fence was placed half way along the open space which stretched all the way down the left hand side of Raglan Gardens. As long as the children could remember, the spot where the fence abutted on to the road was called the 'Boo-Boo Place'. Going back many years to when they were tiny tots, they recalled that they used to scream with delight every time they approached the fence. For hiding behind it Mr. Learner would emerge making a frightening face and shouting "Boo! Boo!"

Jim still remembered the happy times by the 'Boo-Boo' fence. Now he and John waited and turned the tables on the three unsuspecting approaching members of the family. "Boo! Boo!": the boys yelled at the tops of their voices.

About a hundred yards past the fence they crossed the road and approached the few houses built on this side of the road. A loud 'honk-honk' sounded from a vehicle some distance down the road and they all turned to watch the approach of the ungainly motorcar. It was a dilapidated UNIC taxi emitting smoke from the rattling exhaust pipe, and accompanied by an intermittent banging, clanging and rattling.

Sitting proudly in the driving seat was Mr. Potter. His wife was with him and they were both attired in long leather motoring coats, leather caps and sported brightly coloured woollen scarves round their necks. Mrs. Potter's face was completely enveloped in a veil stretching from the top of her cap to under her chin.

The children were delighted to recognise the Potters who lived in Dagmar Avenue. Mr. Potter eked out a precarious living plying for hire outside Wembley Town Station. He was a great favourite with the Learner children who now waved excitedly to him as he coaxed the 'old lady' lovingly homewards.

When the taxi had chug-chugged and phut-phutted its way back home, an aura of complete silence and tranquility descended upon Raglan Gardens. Not a horse-drawn or motorised vehicle was to be seen or heard anywhere in the vicinity. A few walkers and pram pushers went by bracing up to the cold and invigorating wind. Peace was absolute.

* * * *

At this moment in time if Mr. Learner had been gifted with second sight he would have been horrified to witness the transformation which had taken place all around him. The quiet solitude of Raglan Gardens was turned into a noisy, bustling smelly thoroughfare of shiny motor cars, sleek red buses, speeding luxury coaches crammed with pleasure seekers and hundreds upon hundreds of anxious-looking pedestrians bound for who knows where?

Raglan Gardens itself was unrecognisable to the poor bewildered wide-eyed Mr. Learner. Now a long straight tarmacadem surface with wide pavements on either side, it was surrounded with an alarming conglomeration of concrete buildings, a sports drome, a conference centre, an outdoor ice-rink, block upon block of high class flats and, only a short distance from Linden Avenue, a mammoth building with twin domes at either end.

Mr. Learner was petrified. The open spaces, the pleasant park, the 'Boo-Boo' place, the tranquil serenity of the area — all had gone. If Mr. Learner had indeed been the possessor of extra-sensory perception, he would by now have been more than thankful to return to the sanity and placidity of his beloved and familiar Raglan Gardens.

Back in the real world he and his children gave their attention to the three or four old houses at the lower end of the winding lane. One of them in particular was always interesting to look at. It was known as The Dutch House. It was built in 1914 for a Mr. Pott, a gentleman who was rarely to be seen living in or emerging from his house. How this fine property came to be called The Dutch House was not clear to the local residents. Some said it had been dismantled in Holland and rebuilt piecemeal on its present site. Painted blue and white, each front window was famed with attractive wooden shutters. The external appearance of the house was distinctly continental. It was unfailingly admired by all who passed by.

They continued into Wembley Park Drive and arrived at the bridge which crossed the River Brent. Father held on to his hat as he peered over the parapet at the swiftly-running river. Today, because of the torrential rain which had fallen during the past few days, the level of the river was high. The whole family spent a few moments observing the rushing waters.

Peter said he wondered if the river would return to its normal level in the next few weeks. Normally in January or even earlier, the surface became flat calm and froze over completely. For some years this had happened enabling them to fish out their ice- skates from the cupboard under the stairs. Ruth, the athletic one, excelled at the art. Jim and John spent most of their time flat on their backs. Little did they know that in years to come they would be gliding very efficiently round and round an artificial rink not very far from where they were now.

They were reminded by their father of the very severe winter they all experienced two years ago. Then the ice on the River Brent was three or four inches thick, the hoar frost on the ground and trees resembling a carpet of snow. Thousands of birds died in the intense cold. Everyone suffered from the freezing conditions and there was a mighty heartfelt relief when a warm spring followed months of real hardship.

By now the Learners had neared the end of their outward journey. Just beyond the river and before climbing the slight incline to Wembley Park Station, they turned into Aeroplane Road. It was not in fact called Aeroplane Road; this was the descriptive title given to it by one of the children some years ago. It was actually a narrow track running parallel to the railway line. The story had it that an aircraft from Stag Lane aerodrome was in distress, and had to make a forced landing on the rough suface of the track. Whether the pilot or the aeoroplane suffered as a result of the bumpy landing was never made clear. To the Learners it would always be known as Aeroplane Road.

They were all, without exception, quite exhausted when they got to the foot of Linden Avenue, before the final climb up to Letchworth. A cup of tea and huge slices of cut-and-come-again cake soon revived their spirits. The walk down Raglan Gardens had been fun, but now the children turned their attention to the various ways they would be spending Sunday evening. Mr. Learner changed once again into clothes suitable for evening church service. Nothing short of serious illness would prevent him doing his duty. He must always follow his edict of attending church morning and evening every Sunday.

Peter goes to the City

"How many machinists do you have at the factory, father?" Peter asked.

"I have a forewoman in charge of two seamstresses and a woman who does button-holing and other odd jobs. Four employees altogether. You'll see them when we get there. I also have a traveller who goes round trying to get more orders for my business, but you won't see him today. Now, hurry up, Peter, we've got a train to catch at five minutes past seven".

EDWARD Learner was just polishing off his eggs and bacon. His wife poured them both a second cup of tea. The three of them were breakfasting in the kitchen with curtains drawn keeping out the rawness of the dark and dismal morning. It was the following Saturday after their walk down Raglan Gardens, and Peter was to be taken on his first visit to his father's factory in the City.

Later that morning Ruth was due to play in an important hockey match for her school against a team of girls from Alperton County School. The boys were going to the cinema.

Breakfast over, father and son repaired to the hall and hastily dressed for the journey. Mrs. Learner fussed round them, reminding Peter to wear gloves and her husband to be sure to put on his woollen scarf, and watched proudly as they went together down the front drive. She could not keep back a little tear as she realised Peter was no longer her little baby. How many mothers all the world over had similar thoughts about their little treasures?

The two 'men' hurried down the avenue and made for the paper shop. Peter waited while his father bought his News Chronicle and a packet of ten Turf cigarettes. This would normally be twenty on a Saturday but he was keeping to his resolution: he was determined to smoke less. Dashing across the road and booking Peter's ticket they arrived on the platform with just two minutes to spare.

Peter felt extremely proud to be standing there with his father. Even though it was only seven o'clock in the morning the platform was fairly crowded with businessmen and other travellers. Peter smiled at Mr. Sanders who lived opposite them in Linden Avenue. He was also 'something in the City'.

In a few minutes the 7.05 for Marylebone steamed noisily into the station. The five or six carriages were all painted in the smart light brown colour of the L.N.E.R. Doors were pulled open. The train was fairly full and Peter and his father had to run a little way down the platform before they could find a compartment with seats to spare. Mr. Learner grasped the door handle and wrenched open the door just as the guard waved his green flat and blew his whistle.

They scrambled into the compartment apologising for falling over the feet of passengers already seated. They were unable to sit together; Mr. Learner squeezed between two bulky men on one side of the carriage whilst Peter sat in a corner seat on the opposite side.

From his corner he was able to observe their progress uninterrupted. As the train picked up speed Peter began to think of the few times he and his brothers and sister had travelled on this particular line. He was quite a seasoned rail traveller. Every day during term time he used his season ticket on the Metropolitan Railway at Wembley Park. The train took him to Harrow-on-the-Hill where he had a twenty-minute walk to his school, the Lower School of John Lyon, on the other side of Harrow Hill.

But the only time he ever used the L.N.E.R. line was on his family's annual trek to the south coast for their week's holiday. They invariably went to Seaford on the Sussex coast. He smiled as he thought about the three or four suitcases standing on the local station platform waiting for the train to take them all on the first stage of their exciting holiday. Father had to struggle with the two heaviest cases at Wembley Hill and all the interchange stations before

Victoria – Marylebone, Baker Street and Oxford Circus. Victoria Station was the worst of all as this necessitated a walk down an apparently endless underground passage to the main line Southern Railway Station.

A carriage acquaintance of Peter's father then leaned over and spoke to Peter; he knew what business Mr. Learner conducted. "This your first visit to Old Street, my boy?"

"Yes, it is, sir and I'm very much looking forward to it". Peter's reply was by no means hesitant or shy.

"This is Peter, my eldest son", said Edward Learner proudly, "he's fifteen next year and he wants to work in the insurance world".

"Insurance, eh?" He smiled broadly at all the other passengers who were listening with interest to the conversation. "Who knows, in years to come he may be instrumental in working out a policy for your business, my friend".

They all found this quite amusing and were surprised when Mr. Learner said: "Well here we are at Marylebone already. That's been a quick journey; it's obvious that talking, rather than reading a paper, passes the time more quickly".

Peter was interested to see the hustle and bustle of a big London terminus at this time of the morning. He was excited but a little nervous as he remembered his mother's instructions to keep close to his father. As they reached the barrier the ticket inspector clipped Peter's ticket; Mr. Learner, of course, showed his season ticket, and exchanged a few words. He was a well known and respected traveller on this line. They walked out of the station, turned down a back street and came out into the Marylebone Road. From there it was only a short distance to Baker Street Station.

* * * *

Descending into the bowels of the earth they waited on the platform of the Metropolitan Line for a train which would take them to Faringdon Street (later changed to Faringdon Station). Occasionally, depending on the time factor, Mr. Learner would go on to the next station which was Barbican. It was equidistant to his factory from either of those stations, but this morning he wanted to show his son a few of the firms whom he supplied regularly with overalls etc.

Emerging from Faringdon Station he pointed to the dome of St. Paul's Cathedral towering proudly over all other buildings in the vicinity. "Isn't that a wonderful sight, Peter? That can be seen from practically every point in the City".

Peter stared with fascination at the magnificence of the structure. "It's the tallest building in the City of London and no building may be taller than St. Paul's by government order", his father continued.

They were now making their way to Cowcross Street, an extremely narrow cobbled lane with barely room for two vehicles to pass each other, before turning into Charterhouse Street followed by Aldersgate Street. At the junction with Clerkenwell Road and Old Street they turned right and walked about a hundred yards along Old Street until they arrived at the end of Chater's Yard, so called because of the paper manufacturers, Grosvenor Chater, who occupied the majority of the buildings in the yard. Here Mr. Learner stopped and pointed down the yard to a large four storey building at the end of the yard.

"There you are, my son; 47A Old Street. My factory".

"It's ten to eight, Father, exactly fifty minutes since leaving our house".

Mr. Learner consulted his own magnificent gold hunter pocket watch. "So it is; there, what did I say, my boy?"

Walking down Chater's Yard Peter looked up at a fourth floor window of his father's factory. "What does C.P. mean, Father?"

"Oh, that stands for Carter Paterson, a carrier firm. When they are in this area they look for that card in my window, which tells them I have a parcel or parcels to be collected".

"Now, you see those ropes hanging with that little platform attached". He pointed to the platform resting on the ground at the foot of the building. Peter nodded. "Well, the Carter Paterson man will give a long toot on his motor horn. And when I hear that I know that the platform is being winched up to my factory floor. I open up my folding doors (pointing upwards) and deposit the parcels, ready packed, onto the platform".

"I see", said Peter, "and the parcel or parcels are already addressed to the firm where they're going. What a jolly good idea, father". He thought for a moment. "Have you ever forgotten to write an address on a parcel?"

Mr. Learner smiled as they entered the building. "Yes, as a matter of fact I did do just that some time ago. The carrier man didn't notice it and hefted the parcel onto his van. It wasn't till some time later I heard the platform swinging against my folding doors. I looked out and there was one of my parcels sitting on it. Looking down into the yard I could see the driver yelling up at me and making writing signs with his hand and arm".

Peter looked up at the tall figure of his father as they both laughed heartily at the incident. There was no lift in the building and they began to climb the stairs. To reach the factory floor, staff, customers and visitors had to negotiate sixty stairs. Mr. Learner reckoned that at the end of a day, with the climb first thing in the morning, going out to lunch, visiting firms for orders (although his traveller did most of the visiting) and leaving the premises at night, he used each step ascending or descending 360 times every working day.

Nearing the top Peter could hear a loud whirring sound as they entered the factory and walked into the 'cubby hole', the name his father gave to his office. It was tiny, musty, dusty and cold. With Peter gazing curiously at all around him, Mr. Learner switched on the wall-mounted electric fire and picked up the post which his forewoman had placed on his desk. His eyes were immediately riveted on one particular envelope. It bore the mark of St. Colomb's Hospital. Opening up the letter with shaking hands he read the contents. Silently thanking the Lord for His goodness he replaced the letter in the envelope. He told himself Emma would be so relieved to hear the good news.

* * * *

"Well, my boy, this is it. This is where I earn the money to pay for our daily bread. Come along, I'll show you round and introduce you to Mrs. Tinsdale".

Rows and rows of shelves holding bales of cottons, twills, alpacas and other various cloths lined the walls of the room which measured about fifty by thirty feet. A number of huge sacks for the disposal of odds and ends of waste material were dumped at one end of the factory.

Edward J. Learner's forewoman was seated at one of the long tables positioned along a wall of the factory. Five industrial sewing-machines and one button-holing machine were distributed one to each table. Mrs. Tinsdale was putting the finishing touches to one of a batch of bib-and-brace sets, and she was startled to see her employer and a young lad standing at her elbow.

With the deafening noise of the machines operated by four inch wide driving belts, it was impossible to know what was going on in the factory more than a few feet away. She rose hastily and smiled politely at the lad.

"This is Peter, my eldest, Mrs. Tinsdale. He's come to see how I earn my daily crust". Mrs. Tinsdale shook hands with Peter. As they passed along the table Peter was fascinated with the dexterity of the other machinists, one of whom was Mrs. Tinsdale's daughter, Matilda, stitching various backs, fronts, sleeves, collars, etc. to make a whole garment.

He was particularly impressed with the young lady operating the button-holing machine. In a matter of seconds a slit was made in a facing edge of an overall and almost in the same instant the edges of the slit were sewn all round with tightly packed cotton edging. Five button holes on one garment were completed in twenty seconds. The buttons were sewn on by hand.

His father then showed him how he himself cut the material for handing on to his machinists; he was solely responsible for dealing with the orders that came in for the number and variety of garments he made. On his bench situated closed to the folding doors where the hoist was operated, he laid out patterns of boiler suits. Twenty or thirty thicknesses of the particular cloth to be used were meticulously laid right across the length of the bench. Precision in laying the patterns (it was like a jig-saw puzzle fitting everything together) was absolutely essential.

The cutting machine was then hoisted on to the bench, and Peter looked on apprehensively as the sinister looking vertical-bladed machine was guided with exact precision along the marked out chalk lines which had been made round each piece of pattern. The operating of the cutting machine was the highlight of his conducted tour.

Back in the cubby hole Peter was shown an order received in the morning post by his father. "Look at this. It's a reply to one of the circulars we dealt with last Saturday afternoon. And it's a very good order — for fifty white cotton jackets from a chemical engineering firm. Who knows you may have folded the particular circular and put it in an envelope.

Peter beamed. "I say, that's jolly good. You know I never really thought much about what happened to the circulars when we posted them. Now I know and it makes the Saturday afternoon job very much more interesting".

While they were talking a sudden blessed silence descended on the factory. Startled, Peter looked through the cubby hole window at the row of machines. "What's happened? Why have all the machines stopped?" he turned and asked his father.

"It's all right — don't worry, the dynamo has been stopped. It's their tea break. They have a ten minute break mid morning and an hour for lunch. But this being Saturday they finish at 12.30 and go off home to lunch. One of the girls usually brings me a cup of tea but I'll go and tell them I'm taking you to my Lyons Tea Shop for our break. "Put on your overcoat. It's a very cold morning and we've got a five minute walk".

They left the office and started the long descent of the stairs. At the bottom of Chater's Yard they turned into Old Street and made their way to the junction with Goswell Road and Aldersgate Street. Passing the premises of S. Maw Son & Sons Ltd. Peter learned these manufacturing chemists were among his father's best customers. Courtaulds, makers of fine fabrics, was another, and most of the hospitals in the area had placed orders for protective clothing at one time or another.

On the corner of Aldersgate Street and Clerkenwell Road they entered one of the many Lyons' Teashops in the City. Shepherding Peter to his favourite table in the window, Mr. Learner took off his old trilby hat. Peter picked up the menu.

"These tables and chairs are exactly the same in all Lyons' Teashops; did you know that, my boy?"

"What exactly do you mean, Father?"

"Well, the tables all have identical patterned tops and are covered with thick glass. They don't bother with table-cloths or mats; it saves them time and money. All the girl has to do is to wipe over the surface with a damp cloth".

The waitress, known as 'Nippy', came up to their table. Her uniform consisted of a black frock with white embellishments on the bodice, a white apron, the familiar little red badge embroidered on the top of her bodice and, the most eye-catching part of her apparel, a saucy black and white cap perched on the back of her head.

She smiled at Peter, and said to Mr. Learner "He's a handsome lad, isn't he? Your son, I'm sure? Takes after his father obviously", she quipped. Peter blushed – he thought the waitress very pretty.

"Oh, Peter's quite a good lad most of the time. Keeps himself fit. But I tell him he'd be a good deal fitter if he did what I did every morning".

"What's that?" said the waitress. She and Mr. Learner were on very friendly terms.

"Have a cold bath. It's one of the best ways I know of keeping fit".

"There you are, Peter, why don't you try it?" The pretty waitress gave Peter a friendly smile, but seeing he was becoming embarrassed she took their order, cleared away some crockery from a previous customer and walked over to the swing doors leading to the kitchen.

They enjoyed their mid morning break and on the way back to the factory, Peter expressed a keen interest in the workings of his father's accounting system. He gazed with awe at the formidable-looking ledger in which all the business accounts, monies received and cheques paid out, were recorded in Mr. Learner's unique handwriting.

Peter's thought tended towards the possibility that he might make a career in the clothing manufactory trade. To his young, unsophisticated mind it looked more glamorous and exciting than the insurance world. Little did he know that in years to come Jim would be working alongside his father.

At 12.30 the blessed silence came upon the factory again. The machines were covered up for the week-end and the ladies bade farewell to Peter. Father switched off all the lights and once again he and his son descended four flights of stairs.

On the journey home Peter told his father he had immensely enjoyed the visit to the factory, and thought how he would make some of his school mates envious with the fascinating stories about the premises at 47a Old Street.

But one thing above all else he was now looking forward to — that meat roly-poly he knew his mother had made for Saturday dinner!

Ruth of the Rockies, Pearl White and the Israelites

WE have seen that Wembley was well served by religious establishments. Christians of all denominations had no excuse for not attending church services if they had a mind so to do. When it came to secular entertainment there was a distinct paucity of pleasure palaces where the local population could indulge themselves.

Wembley Central boasted one cinema. There was no theatre and no music hall. When local and peripheral residents had seen the two films (one showing on Mondays, Tuesdays and Wednesdays and one on the remaining days of the week) they were left to their own devices as to how they could fill in their leisure hours.

Not everybody fancied patronising the public houses in the district. The Learners, who had lived in Wembley Hill since 1907, had never seen the inside of one of these 'disreputable smelly drinking houses', as Mr. Learner called them. He insisted that his children should be regular attenders at meetings of the Band of Hope. There they were persuaded to Sign The Pledge. It mattered not at all that not one of them had the faintest idea what this act of signing signified. They had signed it; ensuring they were proof against imbibing alcoholic beverages for all time.

The obvious solution for people who required entertainment, not of the extra-mural type, was to make it for themselves in their own homes. They sang songs around the piano, told stories, read poetry and sat round the fire roasting chestnuts and toasting crumpets. Most of these types of entertainment were indulged in from time to time by the Learner family.

Young Jim Learner enjoyed all these various ways of having a good time, but if he was asked to choose between riding on the top of a tram, listening to the band in the park or visiting the local cinema, he would plump every time for the cinema. If there was a different programme every day of the week he would, if circumstances permitted, be sure to pay his threepence or sixpence to enter the magical portals of the cinema.

John enjoyed going but he was not quite as enthusiastic as his younger brother. Ruth, who read every issue of Film Weekly from cover to cover, loved going to the 'flicks' as often as possible, but playing hockey for her school took preference even to the romance of the silver screen. Peter, frankly, was not bothered. He would just as soon be unravelling the mystery of one of Edgar Wallace's latest thrillers.

And so it came about that on this Saturday morning Jim and John, household chores carried out to mum's satisfaction, set off for their visit to the Wembley Hall Cinema. Making their way to John and James's they surrendered their well-washed jam jars to the every-pleasant Mr. Devenish. Three empty two-pound pots entitled them to the princely sum of threepence. Equally six empty one-pound jars meant they were handed another threepence. One penny for each two-pound pot and a halfpenny for every one-pound pot; a financial arrangement which suited both parties admirably. An entrance fee of threepence for the Saturday performance was the open sesame to two and a half hours glorious entertainment.

* * * *

The cinema stood on the corner of Wembley High Road and

Cecil Avenue. The official title of this uninspiring building, architecturally speaking, was the Wembley Hall Cinema, but the local lads and lassies, in the carefree manner of youth, dubbed it either the flea pit or the bug hutch and sometimes both. It had actually started its life in 1911 as a roller-skating rink and it was transformed into a cinema in 1915.

To be absolutely certain of obtaining one of their favourite seats Jim and John would queue for anything up to half an hour in all weathers. Approaching the cinema on this occasion John saw three rough-looking boys, obviously all together, standing by the front entrance.

"Look, Jim, it's Jack Thorpe with those other two boys, Len Wilson and Colin Thompson". He held on to Jim's arm. "We'll hang back a bit and wait till they've gone in".

"Oh gosh, so it is", Jim said, "and with some of those other boys round them that means we shan't get a good seat". They hung about a little distance down the road. Five minutes later it began to rain.

"Come on, John, we can wait round the corner by the exit door. There's a bit of shelter there". No sooner had they made a dash for the door when they saw, to their great relief, that the commissionaire had opened the main door. Dashing round the corner of Cecil Avenue they ran in on the tail end of the two dozen or so children rushing into the foyer.

They paid their threepences at the ticket office and joined in the general pandemonium which followed. Jack Thorpe and his cronies commandeered the three best seats in the front row, crowing with delight at the cleverness of their action. Jim and John thought it expedient to sit well away from the detestable trio.

For the next fifteen minutes certain seats were occupied by excited youngsters and immediately abandoned with a crash when they decided to sit somewhere better. All this time more and more children, one or two accompanied by adults, took their seats in the auditorium. The dingy interior of the cinema was now throbbing with light and excitement in anticipation of the delights to come.

Suddenly a resounding cheer went up as Walter, the commissionaire, made his appearance advancing with measured tread down the central aisle. Reaching the front of the seating accommodation he walked to the end of the platform and climbed the three or four wooden steps on the stage.

Covering the screen was a white canvas sheet bearing the names of local traders. Each trader had his own little box, some eighteen inches square, showing his name and the type of trade he followed. Everyone in the audience knew all the names off by heart and Walter proceeded to carry out his duty with encouraging shouts from all and sundry. As the canvas sheet was slowly rolled up to reveal the magical silver screen, shouts of "Good old Walter" rose to a crescendo.

With the revealing of the screen excitement rose almost to fever pitch. But not quite. The pianist made her appearance from the wings and proceeded to open up the lid of the upright piano. Delving into her music-case she placed several sheets of music on top of the instrument. Excitement knew no bounds.

"Good old Molly".

"Get that piano stool right. You might fall off".

"Have you got the right music with you".

These and other ribald comments, shrill whistles and cat-calls never failed to greet the long-suffering Molly, but she took it all in good part. At last a sort of silence descended upon the auditorium as the pianist played a few opening bars, and as flickering images appeared on the screen John excitedly nudged his brother's elbow "It's Ruth of the Rockies, Jim".

Jim was sucking a pear drop; he was keeping his gob-stopper for the main film. He made no reply but riveted his eyes on the screen as the heroine, dressed in leather jacket with tassles hanging from pockets and sleeves, knee length leather boots and a nondescript dog at her heels, entered a mean hut at the foot of the Rocky Mountains.

The scene within depicted an old, old man, obviously at death's door, lying shivering on a ramshackle old bed. He was covered with a thin blanket. As Ruth went up to the bed and fell on her knees beside the reclining figure, the pianist played suitable pianissimo chords as background music. The old dog whimpered at the foot of the bed.

"Don't die, Father. Don't die. I can't live without you".

The words appeared on the screen well after they had been uttered by the stricken girl, and remained there for at least half a minute. The impression was given that the doltish audience was only able to read with great difficulty, but they wanted to know if the old man died. Tears were seen in the eyes of some of the younger children. As this was only a five minute 'quickie' for openers, the audience knew they would have to wait till next week for the answer to this great drama.

There followed a newsreel showing items of national and foreign news. The British Prime Minister strutted about the streets of a deprived coal-mining area at incredible speed. Soldiers marched through a town in Germany at a pace which would leave the Durham Light Infantry standing. Descriptive captions were displayed on the screen, but the action was so fast there was barely time to take in everything that was happening.

The next 'shortie' developed the continuing action of last week's episode of Pearl White, the beautiful, frail, ashen-faced heroine who had been left tied to the railroad track by a bunch of evil villains.

The lights of the cinema went up. There was an immediate mad scramble for toilets or ice-creams, and a babble of voices echoed round the interior. After the five-minute interval came the highlight of the programme. The main feature film was scheduled to run for an hour and a quarter. Once again all eyes were glued to the screen as men, horses and chariots milled about on an open plain.

Almost immediately the screen went blank. Cries of disbelief, hooting, shouting and derisive cat-calls welled up from the entire body of the hall. The hapless projectionist could be seen struggling manfully in his little cubby-hole to get things right. Within about thirty seconds a slow handclap started. Nobody thought to put on the lights. The shouting and boo-ing got louder and louder. The cinema manager climbed on to the stage to make an appeal for patience, and at that precise moment the projector sprang to life

81

again. The manager ducked as the beam of light shone full on his face, then made a hasty exit.

In the meantime the film had proceeded, but not on the screen. It transpired later that the projector bulb had blown, consequently losing quite a few lengths of reel. But there was no turning back. They were now faced with the sight of hundreds of chariots racing towards the fleeing Israelites, with a fearsome-looking Pharaoh in the leading chariot. The perspiring pianist was playing a remarkably effective rhythmical strumming to give the effect of pounding horses' hooves.

The story of Moses and the parting of the Red Sea was immensely exciting right until the final shot of the Israelites looking back at the plight of the Egyptians. As 'THE END' appeared on screen every wooden seat in the auditorium shot back, sounding like a regiment of drums being beaten. The noise was deafening as the pianist started to play the National Anthem, but very few stood to attention, most of the occupants of the front rows scrambling towards the exits.

John and Jim waited for a few bars to be played but were unceremoniously pushed into the aisle by others waiting to get out. They joined the stream of people emerging from the cinema and into seemingly strong daylight.

"Good, wasn't it Jim?"

"Coo, did you see those horses struggling in the water?"

"Yes, D'you think they all died".

"Gosh, I hope not".

Discussing the film animatedly the brothers wandered home in a gloriously happy frame of mind.

BOOK 2

Aunt Peggy

ONE week before Christmas Day Emma Learner and her four children stood on the down platform of Wembley Hill Station. They were muffled up to the ears in warm overcoats, thick gloves, woollen scarves and hats or caps. It was extremely cold with a bitter east wind blowing. At three o'clock in the afternoon darkness was already falling caused by lowering snow-laden clouds.

As there was no waiting room on the platform they had to keep themselves as warm as possible. Jim and John ran races to the end of the platform and back. They felt wonderfully free; schools had broken up and there were no more lessons for ten glorious days.

Peter and Ruth walked to and fro, stamped their feet and banged their gloved hands against their sides. Mrs. Learner tried to keep her hands warm inside her muff. Even though she had on her best ankle-length winter overcoat and plenty of warm woollies underneath, she was cold.

Suddenly Peter shouted: "Here she comes. I saw some smoke and I think I heard a whistle".

All heads turned to look at the spot where the rails curved round out of sight. There was a louder whistle and as the train came into view the youngsters' excitement knew no bounds – Aunt Peggy (Margaret Caroline Learner) their favourite Aunt, would soon be here. She was going to spend two weeks with them and would be joining in all the fun and festivities of the Christmas holiday. She had been to Letchworth on many occasions but never for Christmas.

Mr. Learner, her elder brother, had seriously contemplated asking his sister to postpone her visit to Wembley for the time being. The extra expense of catering for her for a whole fortnight seemed out of the question in the straitened circumstances in which he had found himself, but the heartening news of the go- ahead for the St. Columb's Hospital order changed everything.

The train drew into the station and with a squeal of brakes shuddered to a stop. When the smoke cleared they could see that only one passenger had alighted. She had two pieces of luggage and was waving frantically at them.

"That is Aunt Peggy, isn't it?" said Jim. "I think she's waving at us".

"I hope it is, otherwise she's missed the train", said Mrs. Learner anxiously. "But she looks so different".

"Come on, Ruth, I'll race you there", said Peter tearing down the platform with Jim, John and Ruth in hot pursuit. They reached the solitary passenger just as the train, with a shrill whistle, pulled away.

"Darlings", said Aunt Peggy. The endearment was followed by a burst of involuntary laughter which, as will be seen, was absolutely unique to this most cheerful of souls. "I couldn't move. I just simply couldn't manage these two on my own. Everybody's been so very helpful at all stages of my journey".

"Auntie, how spiffing that you could come for Christmas", said Peter, putting his arms round her neck and hugging her tight, followed by the two youngest boys.

"Aunt Peggy", said Ruth, not to be outdone in the hugging, "you're sharing my bedroom. I'm so excited I can hardly wait to show you my new gym outfit".

"That'll be lovely, Ruth dear". She went up to Emma who had just reached the merry throng, and threw her arms round her sister-in- law. They embraced lovingly; there was real affection between the two of them.

"Emma dear, how lovely to see you. It's been a long time; there'll be so much to talk about. But my dear, you look absolutely frozen".

"I'm shrimmed to the marrow, my 'ansome", Emma replied in

broad Cornish. Aunt Peggy exploded with laughter. She knew she was in for a lot of this sort of talk during her holiday.

Emma picked up one of the pieces of luggage. It was a large wicker-work basket, closely plaited, with a top lid which fitted right over the bottom container. The whole was kept in place with two stout straps joined together by a strong leather handle.

"Goodness me, whatever have you got in here?" exclaimed Emma, staggering slightly. Another explosion. Aunt Peggy's laugh could be described as the sound made by the sudden emission of air from a motor-car tyre.

"Oh, my dear,isn't it dreadful, I've brought a lot of my piano music with me. Edward said he wanted me to play quite a bit".

"Lovely, Peggy dear. Won't that be lovely, children?"

"Yes" chorused the happy children as they hurried towards the exit.

* * * *

Turning into Wembley Hill Road it started to snow. A few flakes at first, but by the time they reached Letchworth it was coming down fairly heavily. Running up the front garden path Jim waited at the front door for the others to join him. He looked at the thin carpet of snow covering road and pavement.

As Aunt Peggy turned into the gateway he called out: "Auntie, isn't it exciting? It's going to be a white Christmas". His brothers and sister echoed his excitement, but Mrs. Learner, who was absolutely frozen by now, didn't look so happy about it. She hurried to unlock the front door and ushered her sister-in-law into the hallway. It was now very nearly pitch dark and as she went to light the gas mantles Ruth dashed into the kitchen to bring the kettle to the boil.

Aunt Peggy looked round at the scene which had been in her mind's eye for most of her journey. "Emma dear, and children, it's wonderful to be here once again. And nothing seems to have changed since my last visit".

"It has, auntie, we've got a crystal set", said John. "We can hear people talking on it from up there". He pointed vaguely towards the heavens.

"A crystal set?" His aunt looked puzzled "Whatever is that?"

"Now, John, your aunt is very tired and cold and must be longing for a cup of tea. That can all be explained later on". She called to Betty in the kitchen: "Betty, leave that now dear. Take your aunt up to your bedroom. She'll have a cup of tea when she comes down".

She took Peggy's arm and gave her another loving hug. "I can't tell you, Peggy dear, how lovely it is to have you here again. And we're goin' to 'ave lots of laughs, arn't we, my 'ansome?"

"Where've ee been all the time, my dear? We're goin' to 'ave fun and good old chin wags, I can tell ee". Peggy emulated her dear Emma with a very good imitation of the Cornish enunciation. The exchange had the children roaring with laughter. As Ruth piloted her aunt up the stairs another snort of choking laughter could be heard drifting downwards. They all knew that their aunt radiated good humour and jollity.

Ten minutes later they were all seated round the kitchen table. Aunt Peggy, a small bag by her side, said she would see to most of her unpacking later. The gas jets were lit, the kitchen range had been stoked up giving out a welcome warmth to all, and the table was laid out with bread, butter, home made jam and two varieties of mother's special home made cakes — the ubiquitous cut-and-come-again cake and a seed cake.

When they'd all finished tea their aunt picked up her bag and began to rummage in it. Out came a small parcel wrapped in brown paper, which she handed to Peter. He quickly ripped off the wrapping to reveal a brown leather purse. It was rounded at the bottom end and had an aperture which snapped open and shut, worked by flexible steel strips concealed in the leather work.

"Thanks, aunt", he said with feeling, "I've never had a purse before. I can keep my pennies in it for ice-creams and things". He rushed round the table and hugged his aunt and gave her a smacking kiss on her cheek. John and Jim had their eyes glued to Aunt Peggy's bag, and another delve into the capacious interior produced a second parcel, slightly larger than Peter's and oblong in shape.

"That's for you, Ruth darling, I do hope you like it".

With a breathless 'Thanks auntie' she took off the wrapping as fast as her fumbling fingers would let her, and from the little oblong box withdrew a length of wide red ribbon, about twelve or thirteen inches in length and fitted with hook and eye at each end of the ribbon. Ruth pushed her thick black tresses back on her head and then fixed the ribbon round the upper part of her forehead. She then did up the hooks and eyes at the back of her head, shook her head vigorously and was delighted to find that her hair was kept in place.

Her aunt smiled at her. "I remember you told me, dear, that your hair was always getting in your eyes when you played hockey".

"You remembered!" Ruth was wide-eyed. "And it'll match the red sash round my gym slip". She, too, careered round the table and hugged and squeezed her aunt. Meanwhile, Mrs. Learner, who had been sitting watching this handing out of presents, said to Peggy: "My dear, the children are loving this but — er — shouldn't these gifts be kept until Christmas Day?"

"It's all right, Emma darling, these are not Christmas presents. I've got something else upstairs for the great day".

She burst into laughter again making the children laugh happily with her. "Now you know why one of my cases was so very heavy; it wasn't only music, you see". Two more packages were withdrawn from her bag. A penknife for Jim with a spike for getting stones out of horses' hooves, and John was wide-eyed with joy to receive a beautiful wooden box containing pens, nibs, pencils and an India rubber.

The sound of a key being inserted in the front door had all the children rushing out of the kitchen. Gifts were temporarily abandoned as each child jockeyed for position to be first to greet father. Mr. Learner had closed the factory early, much to the delight of his staff, in order to be home early to see his sister. Joyful shouts and laughter were heard in the hallway and then he was dragged into the kitchen by several clinging hands, still wearing his overcoat.

Disengaging himself from his children's grasp, Mr. Learner was quickly at his sister's side. A fond embrace was followed by a long, long look at her.

"You're looking well, Pegsy, but I think you've lost a little weight since I saw you — when was it? — nearly a year ago".

"Lovely to be here again, Edward, and I can see you're still much too thin".

"Oh, nonsense". They hugged again joyfully as the children watched their obvious fondness for each other with great interest. Mr. Learner moved over to his wife and as they kissed lovingly, the children gathered round to show him their gifts.

"Come along, Ruth — Peter — John take your presents upstairs and stay there until I call you down for supper". Despite their protests Mrs. Learner was firm. "I mean what I say, your father wants a quiet cup of tea and we grown-ups have got a lot to talk about. Off you go".

A blessed peace descended on the kitchen. The three 'grown-ups' let their hair down and talked of Mr. Learner's family in Redhill in Surrey. Peggy relieved her brother with the news that their mother was recovering after a nasty attack of choking.

They went on to talk of neighbours and friends at home, and then switched to Peggy's journey to Wembley. "All went well until I got to Victoria. A porter helped me with my baggage and passing through the ticket barrier I realised I would have to spend a penny". They both smiled sympathetically; they knew of Peggy's aversion to using 'one of them awful toilets' on the train.

"He very kindly said he would stay by my luggage until I had finished. It was very embarrassing but what could I do? Going down into the lavatory below ground I fished a penny out of my purse and tried hard to push it into the slot on the door, but it wouldn't go in; something was stuck in there and try as I would the wretched penny wouldn't budge".

"Well...", she burst out laughing, "I was getting desperate and fortunately a woman attendant saw my quandary".

Peggy took hold of Emma's hand and shook with helpless laughter. "Emma, do you remember telling me of that time in the West End of London when you couldn't work the sliding handle on a convenience door?"

Emma nodded and laughed with Peggy at the remembrance of

that episode. "You asked her where you should put your penny and the woman replied 'in my 'and'".

The three of them laughed companionably together. Emma had the wonderful gift of being able to imitate accents and inflections of voice to a remarkable degree. "Well my woman didn't exactly say that but she took my penny and unlocked the door with her master key".

"Poor Peggy. You must have been so relieved", said Edward with unconscious humour.

"And was your luggage all right when you came up again", Emma asked.

"Oh, my dears, no it wasn't. I got such a fright. Getting to the top of the steps I looked where the porter had been standing, but there was no sign of him or of my luggage. I looked all round frantically and just as I thought my luggage had gone for good I heard a shrill whistle coming from the direction of a tobacco kiosk – oh, it must have been some distance away. Peering through the milling crowds on the concourse I spotted my man, the luggage at his side, waving unconcernedly at me.

"He said he'd been getting under people's feet so he had to move. I can tell you I was so relieved to see my luggage again I gave him an enormous tip of sixpence".

"And well worth it, my dear. I'm quite sure that experience and the long tiring journey must be having an effect on you", Emma said solicitously. "Now why don't you go up to your room, send Ruth down and have a nice quiet lie down. That'll do you the world of good".

Peggy nodded: "You're quite right dears. As a matter of fact I've got a splitting headache. I think I will go up for a while".

They got up. Emma put her arm round Peggy's shoulder and Edward opened the door. As she climbed the stairs Peggy smiled to herself as she thought how much she was looking forward to the next couple of weeks. Little did she know what tragedies there were to be in the home before the fortnight was out.

Fun and Reminiscences

EDWARD Learner knew that Peter was normally as quiet as a mouse when reading or studying in his bedroom. Ruth was busy helping her mother prepare the supper, so that left Jim and John.

Knowing that they frequently argued, had pillow fights and occasionally came to blows in their bedroom, he walked in on them suddenly to warn them to be absolutely quiet. He need not have worried. They were erecting a model of a crane from the bits and pieces of a Meccano set strewn all over the floor. Satisfied, he put a finger to his lips, shook his head at them and went downstairs again.

He had changed into a comfortable linen jacket and was wearing his favourite carpet slippers. He was the type of man who looked well dressed, whatever he happened to be wearing. He put the finishing touches to the supper table and decided to have a well-earned cigarette in the peace of the dining room.

The fire was lit and gave out a welcoming warm glow. He didn't bother to light the gas mantles just yet and he puffed away contentedly, smiling as he looked round at the few decorations already put up for Christmas. The children had spent quite a lot of time making the room look cheerful. Sprigs of holly had been placed on the tops of the few pictures in the room. With their own pocket money they had bought several packets of coloured paper measuring about ten inches long by an inch wide and made a paper chain which was hung from one side of the room to the other. Chains had also been hung diagonally across the room and looped across each wall. The whole effect was really quite cheerful.

Finishing his cigarette Mr. Learner was about to have a little nap when he heard his sister moving about upstairs. Guiltily opening the window to let out the smoke – he knew his wife thought he smoked too much – he left the room to join his wife and daughter in the kitchen.

Feeling quite rested and with headache gone Aunt Peggy made her way to the top of the stairs. Passing the boys' room she paused to listen to an extraordinary song proceeding lustily from young healthy lungs. They must have heard their aunt moving about and knew they were free to give voice to the song which went something like this:

"Six o'clock of a shining morn
"We start our busy day.
"We wash the dishes and clean the fishes
"And put the pots away.
"Oh, who would be an orderly
"Upon an orderly day?
"Oh, orderly, orderly, oh the orderly day,
"Poor sore orderly, with a tra-la-la-la-la
""Tra-la-la-la-la-la.
"And it's 'Orderly - squish! Orderly -tosh!
"Orderly, tea this way.
"Oh, who would be an orderleee
"Upon an orderly day?"

An intrigued Aunt Peggy was unable to resist peeping at her two darling nephews giving vent to such a lively song. Knocking softly she entered to be confronted with the picture of Jim and John sitting cross-legged facing each other on one of the beds. They were wearing their Cub and Scout caps on the backs of their heads and drumming their fists on their knees to the rhythm of the song. Seeing their aunt staring open-mouthed at them they grinned sheepishly. John explained it was one of the songs they sang round the camp fire.

"I think it sounded most amusing, dears; I'd love to hear it again", enthused their aunt. Both boys grinned again, looked at each other and started off somewhat shyly, getting increasingly confident as they could see their wonderful aunt was really encouraging them to sing it again.

At the end of the camp fire ditty Aunt Peggy was roaring with laughter. She cuddled both of them and they clung to her happily as they noisily made their way down the stairs. Mr. Learner led the way into the dining-room, which exuded warmth, comfort and a feeling of being happily lived in. The curtains were drawn against the cold and the snow and, as an additional source of light, the magnificent brass oil-lamp, polished until it positively glittered, gave out a diffused glow from the sideboard.

The plates heaped with generous slices of beef, boiled potatoes, sprouts, cabbage and the whole covered with thick meaty gravy, were put in front of the family and their most welcome guest.

The conversation was limited to asking for the salt to be passed or for another glass of water and it was not until the second course (tapioca pudding) had been summarily dealt with that they felt inclined to talk about anything else other than food.

Normally at the end of each meal Emma insisted the washing-up be dealt with immediately. But this evening, in deference to her guest, she began reminiscing on some of the amusing events affecting the family that had taken place in Wembley and further afield. Edward and the children knew from past experience that they were in for a treat.

Turning to Peggy she said "Remember the time, oh several years ago when the children were tiny and you took them down Raglan Gardens in the large pram we used to have". She stopped as Aunt Peggy began to explode with huge bursts of uninhibited laughter.

"You mean when I upset the pram and they all fell out on the pavement". She tried to look horrified and amused at the same time.

"Not me", Peter said. "I wasn't in the pram; I was walking beside it and helped you to get them back in again". He grinned hugely at the memory. The rest of the family were consumed with merriment.

Even Edward, who was not given to a great deal of hearty laughter, joined in the chorus.

Peggy was beside herself. "I'll never be able to live that down, I mean just imagine, you might all've been killed". But she wasn't allowed to feel badly about it for very long as Emma quickly changed the subject.

"Nonsense, my dear, it was just one of those things. Probably happens to lots of children. Now, do you remember the last time you were here, you and I did a bit of shopping in the High Road?"

"Yes, I do". Peggy nodded. "Wasn't that the time we bought the new curtains for the drawing-room? In Killip's wasn't it?"

"That was it, and they were a real bargain. But we also went into Mr. Dunn's the boot mender; and I needn't remind you about him!"

Peggy chortled. "Mr. Dunn! What a character. I nearly died when you innocently spoke to him in an accent remarkably similar to the one he used. I didn't know where to put my face, I wanted to burst out laughing".

Emma smiled: "Well, I took a pair of Edward's shoes in only last week and Mrs. Dunn was in the shop with her husband. We talked about the weather and as you know, she has rather an affected way of speaking. She said "We took the car out last week for a little run but the weather! – it began to pour and by the time we got the hood up we were nearly soaked".

Emma explained that Mrs. Dunn's manner as well as her speech was inclined to be pseudo grand. "We still had a way to go but – where was we, Charlie, when the rain come on? We was to St. Albans, wasn't we, Charlie?"

'Yaaas', was Charlie's succinct reply".

Emma's imitations had them all holding their sides with shrieks of laughter.

"'Anyway we decided to carry on and ... what was that noise downstairs Charlie!' A scrambling scratching noise followed by a dull thud could be heard in the basement of the premises. Charlie's facial expression could only be described as demonic.

"'Wait 'alf a minute, Mrs. Learner, that's my blooming' cat got 'old of a lump of my beef'. He went down the stairs at the speed of light. Then followed a series of bangs and slaps interspersed with loud howling 'Miaaoows'. What the poor cat of theirs went through, I don't know", Emma said as the others wiped their eyes weak with laughter.

But now she could see that time was getting on and they still hadn't had their after supper cup of tea.

She said to Peter: "Go and boil up the kettle, dear, I know your auntie would love a nice cup of tea". Peter reluctantly left the room; he didn't want to miss any of the fun.

Then Emma told the oft-repeated story of the time in London's West End when she was shopping with a friend from up the hill.

She went on:- "The streets were crowded with buses and cars and my friend and I decided to have a cup of tea in a Lyons' Tea Shop on the other side of Oxford Street. I stepped off the curb behind a bus which had stopped to pick up passengers. Another bus which was following behind came up quickly and stopped only a few feet from me.

"I was terrified. My friend had already got across but I was left stranded, because of traffic coming from the other direction, between these two huge buses. The driver of the bus which had just come up opened his cab window, leant out and shouted 'Lor, luv yer ma, yer'd make a luvly 'am sandwich!'"

Aunt Peggy exploded. Although they'd heard it so often before the others were doubled up with laughter. Emma was smiling and said "I shall never forget the indignity of that moment as long as I live".

"That was so funny", her sister-in-law said when she had recovered from her paroxysm, "You're absolutely wonderful the way you tell those stories. And I know they really are true, perhaps with a little bit of trimming". She smiled at Emma: "But Emma dear, do tell us that hilarious tale about your sister Maisie in Falmouth".

Emma laughed out loud. "You mean the time she and some of her friends went to a revivalist meeting in the town?"

Peggy nodded her head eagerly. Although this tale also had been heard many times before it lost none of its hilarity in the re- telling.

Putting down a cup of tea Emma said: "Well this revivalist meeting was held about once a month in the Chapel Hall. It was taken quite seriously by the majority of the audience who loved the stirring hymns and the fiery sermons given by dedicated speakers. The object of the meetings was to ensure the souls of the people present were saved from damnation".

Edward chuckled out loud as he recalled the way in which this particular meeting had developed. Aunt Peggy was regarding her dear Emma with bated breath.

Emma went on. "The worshippers, simple upright people of this Cornish port, usually consisted of men and women of a mature age. Therefore the organisers were not a little surprised to see, and welcome, five or six youngish females who came into the hall and seated themselves in a row towards the back. My sister Maisie, one of the young ladies, sat at the end of the row next to the gangway.

"The speaker on this particular evening was a tall solemn bearded gentleman dressed in a severe black suit. Not a touch of colour in his clothing relieved his sombre appearance. His lengthy sermon was on the subject of inevitable hell and damnation unless those present repented and asked forgiveness for their sins.

"My sister and her friends were hard put to it not to dissolve into fits of giggling. The sermon over, the speaker descended into the body of the hall and asked every single person present if he or she was prepared to be saved from the most awful fate. Approaching the back row he came up to Maisie and started to ask her the same question. But Maisie forestalled him and said in a very loud voice: "All saved in this row, sir!"

"A few of the assembled audience burst out laughing but the majority looked on with frowning disapproval. They took their prospects of avoiding eternal damnation seriously. The speaker obviously did not know how to handle this situation. He glowered at Maisie, his beard quivered indignantly and he stormed back to the platform. Maise gave a sign and they all rushed from their seats and escaped through a side door".

Aunt Peggy could hardly control herself; she was doubled up, helpless with laughter. The others were just as bad; the noise of simple merriment filled the room. It was Emma herself who took the matter in hand and began to clear the supper table.

"I don't know where my dear wife gets her amazing gift from", Edward said to his sister, "I've known her for over twenty years and she can still make me laugh with the same stories I've heard over and over again".

Still chuckling happily the family completed clearing the supper table. Edward damped down the fire and turned off the gas mantles. Soon their voices could be heard in animated conversation between the kitchen and the scullery. The Learners were hard at it doing the washing-up.

Christmas Eve

THE next day, Christmas Eve, the children's favourite aunt demonstrated two further sides of her character. They already knew of her unfailing good humour and jollity. During the next few hours they were to witness an almost boyish love of playing pranks.

Later in the evening they were to watch entranced as she bent over the keys of her brother's beautiful piano. Her normally smiling countenance would be tranposed into one of beatific serenity; she played with absolute concentration, obviously straining every fibre of her body. In short she was a lady of incredibly diverse moods.

After breakfast that morning when Jim opened the back door he gave a shout of delight. The snow overnight had been falling thick and fast. His world was covered with three or four inches of lovely glistening pure white snow.

During the washing-up plans were made for the ensuing day and, Mrs. Learner told the children she wanted them to do some shopping. Most of the shops opened at half past seven in the morning – and a few even before that – but she didn't expect her offspring to be ready by that time. Included on the list which she entrusted to Peter were some raisins, sultanas, candied peel and flour for her Christmas puddings. Cries of delight greeted mother's announcement that Aunt Peggy would be invited to join the children later on that day in stirring the 'Christmas puds'.

As long as they could remember, stirring the Christmas pudding at night time in their dressing gowns just before going to bed, was one of the greatest joys of the festive season. Now they were all growing up the ceremony was performed during daylight hours in a lovely warm steamy kitchen. Mother always wore her wrap-around apron and her arms were bare as she struggled to control an immense mixing-bowl on the kitchen table.

Later in the day when they returned from the shops they would go with their aunt into the park for a walk and no doubt for snow-balling.

The three others waited outside as Peter went into Hills' the chemist for a bottle of quinine and a jar of Extract of Malt. Jim told his mother the previous evening he felt he had a 'bit of a throat'. She took his temperature and felt his forehead and although the temperature was normal, and he said he felt fine that morning, she was not going to take any chances. The medicine was there if it was needed. Mr. Hills waved to them cheerily as they all moved off.

Glancing at his list Peter announced the next item was a box of King George the fifth chocolates. These could only be obtained from Interbitzens. Four mouths watered involuntarily as these delicacies materialised before their minds' eyes. They knew these delicious chocolates were a very special treat for Christmas. Normally a visit to Mr. Janes for a couple of gob-stoppers or an ounce of bullseyes would be the extent of their shopping for sweets.

The presence in Wembley Hill of a shop by the name of Interbitzens was considered curious by the locals. It was generally thought to be of Swiss origin. Whether this was the name of the original owners or the name of a region in Switzerland, nobody knew. All Ruth and the others knew was that the window display in that establishment was tantalising to their young eyes. When Jim was much younger and had heard his father say he was going to this particular shop, he mystified the family and caused them much merriment when he asked if they sold liquorice sticks at 'Interbitches!'

Emerging from Interbitzens with the precious confection tastefully wrapped in a piece of plain white paper, Peter said he had been told to buy a few fancy cakes from Eldridges. He handed the chocolates to Ruth who was carrying the shopping basket.

Meanwhile Jim and John tried to warm themselves up with a bit of snow-balling. Even with thick stockings and good Wellingtons their feet were getting frozen. Running out into the road to avoid a huge snowball John threw at him, Jim miraculously escaped being hit by a motorised van passing by. The driver sounded his hooter and waved a furious fist at the shaken lad.

Snow-balling was abandoned as they all filed into Watson's, the fruiterer and greengrocer. They loved the sight of all the different fruits and vegetables tastefully displayed, and the smell was gorgeous. Peter had been strictly ordered to buy only Sahara dates in a nice box and a pound of mixed nuts. Excitement knew no bounds for the children knew all these goodies were to be consumed over the Christmas holiday.

Mr. Watson had the monopoly of the fruit and veg trade in Wembley Hill. Emma often remarked to Edward that she wondered how he was ever able to make a profit. She knew that as each child filed out of the shop he would be presented with a shiny red apple; and apples were 4d. a pound! But some said there was method in his madness; such acts of kindness ensured the retention of valued customers. It was then on to John and James's where the amiable Mr. Devenish saw to Mrs. Learner's order for the Christmas pudding 'gredients', as Jim put it.

* * * *

Shopping completed they trudged homewards through the ever-thickening snow which was by now beginning to get churned up. Aunt Peggy was greeted as though she was a long lost friend. The shopping basket was deposited on the kitchen table, and after checking the purchases Emma expressed her complete satisfaction with everything that had been bought. Peter handed her the change from the pound note she had entrusted to him.

She then checked the price of each item very carefully and said to him: "There's a shilling short, Peter. Are you sure that's all you've got in your pockets?"

Peter went very red in the face as he became aware of everybody looking at him. "I haven't got any money left, mother, honestly I haven't". He emptied his pockets even pulling his trousers pockets inside out. "Perhaps you've made a mistake in the price of something?"

"Oh, no, I haven't", Emma said, "now you go through everything with me". They proceeded to check each purchase item by item. The result was the same.

"Well I expect somebody overcharged me a shilling", Peter said indignantly. "in any case I've told you that's all the change I had left". He looked defiantly at his mother.

"Perhaps you dropped a shilling in the snow, dear", Aunt Peggy said helpfully. She hoped there would not be any unpleasantness. Ruth and John nodded at this. They were anxious to drink a glass of milk with their biscuits and get off to the park, but now they saw that Emma was looking closely at Jim. She noticed that he was trying not to be noticed as he stared hard out of the window.

"Jim! Why are you so quiet".

He wriggled in his seat as he realised all eyes were on him now. Suddenly he burst into tears and guiltily took a shining shilling out of his trouser pocket.

"I saw Peter drop it, mummy, and I did so want to buy some sweets to give to dear Auntie Peggy".

He was sobbing uncontrollably, gulping down the tears and looking as miserable as sin. Peggy was going to put her arms round the unhappy boy, but Emma stopped her.

"No, Peggy, I won't tolerate dishonesty. It doesn't matter what the ulterior motive was going to be. Jim was very wrong to allow Peter to be suspected of keeping money for himself. Go upstairs, James. There'll be no going to the park for you and I'll have to speak to your father about this".

Emma was very angry. Without a word Jim sobbed his unhappy way upstairs, leaving behind a somewhat glum assembly round the kitchen table. The incident left a nasty taste in their mouths for some time to come.

Aunt Peggy was all for spending the rest of the morning in the house with the other three children. She was quite upset at the idea of leaving poor little Jim crying miserably in his bedroom. But Emma was adamant.

"You go off to the park with them, my dear. It'll do young James no harm to reflect on his naughtiness for a while. I'll call him down when you get back and he can help with stirring the pudding".

Emma loaned Peggy a pair of her Wellingtons which she dragged from the back of the cupboard under the stairs. As it happened they wore the same size. Milk and biscuits finished they wrapped up warmly again and the four of them – Peter, Ruth, John and Aunt P. – climbed the hill through the snow to the top of Linden Avenue.

* * * *

Nearly all the neighbours were industriously sweeping the snow from their front drives. Piles of it were deposited in heaps in the gutters at the side of the road. The kiddies in the neighbourhood, all in holiday mood, were having a wonderful time throwing snowballs at all and sundry; making huge snowballs to be eventually rolled down the steep hill and cramming handfuls of the stuff down unsuspecting friends' necks, only to get the same treatment themselves in an unguarded momemt.

It was a very happy scene which Peggy and her charges delighted to witness. They ran down the slope on the other side of the hill with their aunt in the lead and, crossing Park Lane, dashed down the steps into the park itself.

King Edward the Seventh park was an extremely pleasant area of grassland, trees, tennis courts, bowling greens and children's playing area. A pavilion built entirely out of wood was scored on every possible surface with the initials of children who had played and sheltered there over the years. During the summer months it was delightful to stroll happily over the lush grass, watch the children on swings and see-saws, sail model boats on the kidney-shaped pond and partake of refreshments in the park cafe.

The Learner children loved to bring a cricket bat, a couple of stumps, one for each end of the 'Pitch', and a cricket ball. Jim was always the first to tire of the game; if he was not allowed to bat he would lie down at the side of the pitch and be told by Peter that he was a lazy little tike. They also spent a lot of time clambering over the cannon which was a relic of the Great War. It was placed on a concrete slab adjacent to the park keeper's lodge.

Frequently the screams and shouts of high-spirited youngsters yelling 'bang' 'bang' as they pretended to be firing shots from the barrel of the cannon would be too much for the long suffering 'parkie'. Emerging from the lodge he approached the offending young varmints, shaking his fist and shouting dire threats. Scattering in all directions they would wait for him to go back indoors and creep back to the cannon as soon as they thought it safe to do so.

Occasionally if the parkie had really had enough, he would surprise them by running from the back of the lodge wielding his fearsome looking stick with the pointed end. This would have the desired effect; the children would disappear emitting shrieks and howls.

Tiring of the cat and mouse game with the park-keeper, they would make for the grassy bank close to the vehicular entrance from Park Lane. In gorgeous sunny weather the four of them would delight in lying down on their sides at the top of this steep bank. Races were held to see who could roll over and over down the bank and get the furthest from the top. Shrieks of laughter accompanied their rolling progress down the incline.

(In later years, looking back on those happy carefree times spent enjoying their simple satisfying childish games, they were firmly convinced that those summer days were forever days of constant glorious sunshine. No one could persuade them otherwise.)

But the most satisfying and absorbing of all their activities was to crowd round the bandstand during the summer season. On fine summer evenings and on most week-ends a Military Band would be playing. Deck chairs could be hired at threepence a time although most people preferred to wander round the outside of the bandstand. The sound of well-loved melodies echoing round the park never failed to draw the crowds. Very often the bandsmen were attired in full dress military uniforms.

It was generally agreed by young and old alike that listening to the band in the park was probably the most pleasant pastime one could hope to enjoy 'for free'.

Few people could remember that the park, prior to 1914, was an area of sloping meadows where cattle grazed and hay-makers were busy in the summer sunshine. Folk who could remember those nostalgic times thought the transformation from meadows to recreation ground a mixed blessing. The Learners were in no doubt at all that they loved their park just as it was.

Today, in company with their favourite aunt, they revelled in making snowballs from the soft fresh snow and pelting one another until their arms were too tired to pick up any more snow. Wending their way back to Linden Avenue they were glad to see, on their arrival home, that Jim had been reprieved. Their mother had changed her mind after having a talk with him in his bedroom. He had convinced her that he honestly had not intended to steal the money, and he just wanted to buy something for Aunt Peggy. Cups of tea, sandwiches and the inevitable slices of cake quickly consumed, the serious business of stirring the Christmas pudding got under way. Four excited children, aunt and mum stood round the mixing bowl. It was a tradition that six shining threepenny bits were placed on a saucer at the side of the mixing bowl, one threepenny bit for each Learner. This year, in honour of their very welcome guest, the number had been increased to seven.

Cries of delight and laughter accompanied each and every dropping of a coin into the heavenly smelling mixture. Young Jim and John particularly knew that the next time these shining objects came into view would be tomorrow, Christmas Day.

And if anybody was lucky enough to discover more than one threepenny bit in his portion, woe betide him if he tried to keep the extra one for himself. One year poor Ruth did not find a single coin on the great day or on any subsequent occasion when further puddings were served up. Father came to her rescue. When she was not looking he fished a brand new threepenny bit from his pocket, asked her to pass the custard which was on the sideboard, and popped it in her unfinished portions of pudding.

* * * *

The excitement of mixing the pudding over, Emma told them she was tired and suggested her sister-in-law take them for a walk into town and, agreeing this was a good idea, they got dressed up again and started off down the avenue.

It had stopped snowing for a while and there was even a glimpse of watery sunshine peeping through the clouds. They took it in turns to cling on to their aunt's hand, skipping happily along towards the High Road. Aunt Peggy told Edward later that evening that each of his children was a delightful chatter-box.

"By the time we got to St. John's Road, my head was buzzing with information about open-top trams, tradesmen's vans, Trojan cars, horses and cabs and things they'd seen in the shops which they'd like for Christmas. I was quite exhausted".

It had been their intention to go on to Killip's shop and have a look at the cash dispenser whizzing to and from the cash desk. But by now the weather was beginning to turn colder again; the sun disappeared and more snow threatened.

"Let's go down to Elm Road and knock on one or two doors, shall we, dears?" said their beloved aunt. Although she was well past her thirtieth birthday this woman of many moods was for ever ready for a bit of fun. The children remembered the last time she came they paid a visit to Elm Road. All the houses, mostly terraced dwellings, had their front doors set back from the frontage of the house. Consequently anyone calling could not be seen by any of the neighbours on the same side of the road. This arrangement suited our intrepid aunt and her four cohorts admirably. Great excitement and suppressed giggles could be heard as they turned into Elm Road.

"I say, auntie", whispered Jim, "Let's call at No. 14. That's the home of old Mrs. Beatty; she always takes ages to answer the door".

"Oh, no dear, we won't call on anybody very old. That wouldn't be fair", Aunt Peggy said firmly.

"What about Miss Matthews at No. 22, she's quite a lively lady", Peter courteously suggested, smiling up at his aunt.

The others agreed and by a tacit arrangement the four youngsters took up their positions in the doorway of No. 18, two doors away from their intended victim. With her finger to her lips Peggy stole past No. 20, looked cautiously into the front window of Miss Matthews' house and made a dash for the doorway. She gave a long rat-a-tat on the door knocker, sped down the drive and ran to join the others waiting breathlessly at No. 18.

She had only just managed to conceal herself when the front door of No. 22 was opened. A mystified Miss Matthews could be seen peering up and down the road, even coming out to her front gate to see who could possibly have been knocking at her door. John nearly burst out laughing peering round Peter's frame, but was shut up just in time by Peter and Ruth. Eventually with a wondering shake of her head the victim of the prank went indoors to sit by the kitchen fire waiting for the caller to knock again.

Some would say this was an unkind prank to play. But Aunt Peggy, who was an ardent Christian and regular worshipper, looked upon it as a harmless bit of fun mainly for the benefit of her nephews and niece. What was quite surprising was that an explosive 'Ah-Pooh' did not give the game away. It was lucky for the pranksters that Miss Matthews was stone deaf anyway.

A Recital

EDWARD was as good as his word and got home by five o'clock. As this was Christmas Eve he had closed the factory early, telling Mrs. Tinsdale that she and her staff should report for work on the day after Boxing Day. Business was picking up again and the order for St. Columb's Hospital would take up the rest of December and well into January.

(In those days a fortnight's break spanning Christmas and the New Year or five or six days holiday at Easter time was unheard of. Management wanted to get on with their business activities and staff were quite content to have a few days rest before returning to work. Any other privileges were not even contemplated).

They sat silently for a while and then Emma said: "I hope Peggy and the children will be back soon; even though it's quite dark now it looks very black outside".

"They'll be alright. Don't forget it takes much longer to get home in the snow. I noticed it's much thicker here than in the City". As he pulled the curtains back to peer through the window there was a knock on the front door. "There they are now".

Emma ran along the passage and opened the door. A frozen group crowded into the hall, snow thick on their coats and hats. They all rushed into the kitchen and stood round the range, gratefully rubbing hands blue with the cold, before going upstairs to change.

"I do hope dear Peggy will be recovered enough to play for us tonight", Emma said. I've already lit the fire in the withdrawing room. It should be quite warm in there by now".

"Don't worry, my dear. I'm sure it will be. Knowing Harriet and Henry are coming tonight I'm certain you've done everything possible to make it cosy in there".

"Well yes I have but you can't be too careful when it's so dreadfully cold outside. But Edward, dear, I'm just longing to see the children's faces when we tell them they're going to be allowed to stay up tonight".

"Yes, and I'm just longing to hear Peggy play again. I can safely say that with few exceptions – and I don't mean myself – she's the most accomplished pianist outside the professional world I've ever heard".

Emma did not entirely agree. She was tremendously proud of her husband's virtuoso performances at piano and organ. He played the piano on every possible occasion at home, and even his children were very much aware of his love for classical piano and orchestral music. Before his marriage he played the organ at the local Parish Church in Crownthorpe, his parents' original home in Norfolk. Neither his mother nor his father were particularly musical. It was therefore quite surprising that both he and his sister Peggy should be so accomplished in the realm of the pianoforte.

* * * *

The supper meal was eaten in an atmosphere of intense excitement; the children were over the moon. It was Christmas Eve with the prospect of stockings being hung up, their beloved Aunt Peggy staying until just before the New Year, being allowed to stay up and listen to father and aunt entertain them on the piano and, an unexpected additional treat, to be sitting with 'uncle' Henry and 'auntie' Harriet from next door who they were all very fond of.

"I want you to promise me that you'll behave yourselves. No giggling and whispered remarks if Uncle Harry says he would like to recite a poem. And there won't be any cracking of nuts because I've made sure there won't be any in the room. I've put a bowl of sweets and chocolates on the side table. Jim and John, you'll have to sit on the floor".

Emma was firm; she was anxious to show her good neighbours that her children could be well behaved when occasion demanded.

The scene was set. The withdrawing room was bathed in a soft light. Only two of the four gas mantles had been lit but an oil lamp was placed in a strategic position for the pianists' convenience. With the glow from the fire the overall atmosphere in the room was cosy and homely. Emma had spent a good deal of the morning polishing and dusting. A few decorations similar to those in the dining-room completed a picture of domestic comfort.

A knock on the door sent her and Edward, with Peter and Ruth in close attendance, hurrying along the hallway to welcome their guests. Coats and hats were hung up on the hall stand, shoes were divested of snow and Mr. and Mrs. Wyatt were ushered into the withdrawing room. Edward introduced them to his sister who remarked that she was delighted to meet them again.

Mr. and Mrs. Wyatt were asked to sit on the only settee in the room — a handsome piece of furniture with a wooden framework upholstered in shiny flowered damask; although handsome it was not the most comfortable item of furniture. Edward, Emma and Peggy sat in individual armchairs. The room had a distinctly Oriental atmosphere; a cabinet filled with Chinese and Formosan objets d'art; the octagonal pagoda-shaped table inlaid with mother-of-pearl (which Harriet prayed she would not be given for her cup and saucer later on) and a beautiful Chinese screen placed by the door to keep out draughts. Peter sat on a tooled leather pouffe whilst Ruth tried to make herself comfortable on the little box stool housing the crystal set. The two boys sat or lay on a thick rug in front of the fire.

After a great deal of persuasion Mr. Learner agreed to be the first to play a 'little something' on the piano. He rarely played from memory and Ruth, who was rapidly becoming quite proficient at the piano, turned the pages of the music score. The strains of one of Beethoven's minuets filled the room. His touch was firm and technically correct, but some said there was a lack of 'soul' in the way he moved and fingered the keys.

However, everyone in the room was obviously enjoying his performance and when he played a moving excerpt from Madam Butterfly, the children's favourite, the rapt expressions on every face spoke volumes. The applause was warm and heartfelt. There followed a beautiful rendering of a Chopin Polonaise after which Edward resumed his seat to renewed applause.

All eyes now turned to a surprisingly nervous Aunt Peggy. Few people, with the exception of brother Edward, could have guessed that even after playing in public on many occasions, she was not a little embarrassed when asked to perform in a circle of friends or even in the bosom of her family The spotlight was taken off her for a few blessed moments when Emma caught Jim surreptitiously trying to sneak a King George the Fifth chocolate from the bowl on the side table.

"Jim! Whatever are you thinking of? You know you should ask before you take a chocolate. Now hand the bowl round to the guests and when everybody's been offered one you can be the last to have one".

Shame-faced, Jim obediently got up and did as he was told. Aunt Harriet, who had been indulging in a spot of 'shut-eye', was effusive in her thanks for the chocolate and was given the opportunity to surface without undue embarrassment.

Meantime, Aunt Peggy, who had been adjusting the height of the piano stool, awaited the necessary silence before she consented to play. Throats were cleared, a hasty cough from Jim was quickly stifled after a glare from mum and once again everyone settled down to hear a performance which the grown-ups knew would be masterly.

She had chosen to wear a loosely-fitting dark blue silk dress and had purposely refrained from wearing jewellery of any description. Her dark brown hair, normally worn free of combs or hairpins, was tonight severely drawn back and kept in place with a wide white headband. Her features were now completely composed. Every one of the Learners was amazed and fascinated to observe the utter con-

111

trast of her present demeanour with the many and varied moods they had witnessed since her arrival.

She played entirely from memory. Her first item was an enchanting piece from Chopin, a Nocturne in F Sharp Minor. As her long shapely fingers caressed the keys her body from the waist upwards swayed to and fro over the keyboard, her eyes closed in complete concentration.

Mr. Learner, who was following the music on the score given to him by his brilliant young sister, could not conceal his generous admiration of her playing. The silvery notes kept pouring from the body of the piano. As the concluding strains of the nocturne were played there was complete silence in the room and then, as if a spell had been broken, tumultuous applause broke out from all in the room. Even young Jim and John were obviously sincere in their loud clapping.

"Bravo! Bravo!" they cried.

She bowed as the applause continued. Uncle Henry was unashamedly enthusiastic in his hearty applause. Accustomed to enjoying the playing of his good friend and neighbour, he was nevertheless aware that this talented young pianist was head and shoulders above Edward Learner in her interpretation of this most difficult of Chopin's compositions.

After a suitable pause for more comfortable positions to be taken up (particularly Jim squirming restlessly on the floor) the Learners and their guests were treated to another masterly rendering, this time of chopin's lively Mazurka No. 17 in B flat. Aunt Peggy's fingers flew over the keys in this triple time composition with incredible speed, and around the room feet and hands kept time to the rhythmical beat. It was all immensely enjoyable.

With the conclusion of this piece Aunt Peggy begged to be excused from performing further, saying she had developed a headache with concentrating so much. As it happened Emma chose this very moment to come back into the room bearing a tray loaded with cups and saucers. She had slipped out unnoticed during the Mazurka.

Ruth and Peter both helped with teapot, milk, sugar and solid refreshments. Peter eyed the plates of fancy cakes he had bought that morning. 'Bags I that one' he thought to himself. (That one happened to be a square-shaped sponge cake about three inches square completely strewn with chopped nuts, covered on top with raspberry jam and the whole adorned with a dollop of real cream; it cost fourpence at Eldridges). He was disgruntled to see Uncle Henry dispose of it in a couple of bites!

Mr. Learner, sitting next to his good friend Henry had persuaded him to recite one of his famous poems after the refreshments.

"My dear friend, I should be reluctant to impose on your hospitality with any poor effort of mine", Henry replied unconvincingly.

He was relieved when Edward said: "Nonsense, my dear chap, you certainly would not be imposing. In fact I feel sure we would all be quite privileged to listen to one of your remarkable renderings". There was not a trace of irony in this well-meant assurance.

"In that case, my dear Edward, I shall be honoured to perform". Henry looked across at Harriet. She had heard the last part of this exchange and beamed her approval at her beloved.

Uncle Henry was a little man, short of stature and, as frequently happened with men of his height, made up in volume what he lacked in size. He wore an immaculate grey suit with waistcoat sporting a gold chain and medallion attached, a spotless white shirt and a smart red bow tie. He now moved to the centre of the room where all could see him and took up an almost aggressive stance in front of the fire. He stumbled over Jim's feet and apologised profusely to the 'dear boy', then told the assembled audience he regretted he had brought no books of poems with him. However if they would bear with him he would recite one or two of his betterknown efforts from memory.

There followed much clearing of the throat and with his feet placed well apart, he said: "One of Samuel Taylor Coleridge's immortal poems from The Rime of the Ancient Mariner". He paused for effect, then began in a very loud voice: ""'The Harbour bay...'" but got no further. The good Henry was stopped in his tracks by the voices of carol singers with 'Good King Wenceslas'

Looking deeply apologetic, Edward mouthed: "My dear Henry,

how unfortunate at this very moment..." and made for the door followed by Ruth, John and Jim. As they could be heard talking and listening to the church carol singers, the others witnessed the spectacle of Henry Wyatt standing with his back to the fire, his mouth opening and closing like a stranded whale. He glared at the door but realising the door wasn't at fault resumed his seat to the sympathetic clucking noises of Aunt Harriet.

Edward and his children came back into the room shivering and made a bee-line for the fireplace. "They were all members of the choir". He said. "I invited them in but they said this was their last call. They wanted to get home and I can't say I blame them".

He turned to his good friend. "Henry, old chap, what can I say? I can only apologise for the untimely interruption of your poem. If we can all get settled again I feel sure there will be no further disturbances".

Mr. Wyatt blew his nose loudly, got to his feet and once again took up his position in front of the fire. He cleared his throat. "One of Samuel Taylor Coleridge's immortal poems from The Rime of the Ancient Mariner". Another pause for effect. Again in a very loud voice:-

> "'The harbour bay was clear as glass,
> So smoothly it was strewn.
> And on the bay the moonlight lay,
> And the shadow of the moon
>
> 'The bay was white with silent light,
> Till, rising from the same,
> Full many shapes that shadows were,
> In crimson colours came.'"

As the verses unfolded Uncle Henry became more and more immersed in the recital he was giving. His voice boomed out and his face was turning a remarkable shade of beetroot red, both from his efforts and from the heat of the room. From their position on the rug Jim and John stared hypnotically up at him. They had never seen him perform before.

After three or four minutes of the loud dissertation, the situation proved too much for Jim; he glanced at John and that did it! A titter soon became an outright giggle. Try as they would neither of them could stop it; to hide their embarrassment they rolled over on the floor and took refuge at the back of the settee. Their chuckles were by now only too audible.

Uncle Henry glared in their direction. Aunt Harriet, for once stung into action, spoke her indignant disapproval. Even Aunt Peggy was unable to see the funny side of things; she looked on horror stricken at the sight of a co-artist being treated in this way.

As though activated by clockwork Edward and Emma got up from their seats and swooped on the luckless chortlers. Jim received a whacking swipe on his posterior administered by a furious mum whilst John was picked up bodily by an irate father and bundled out of the room.

Uncle Henry plodded remorselessly on with the continuing tale of The Ancient Mariner but eventually realised he was no longer the cynosure of all eyes. From the hall came angry sounds and howls of pain and sobs were clearly heard as the youngsters made their miserable way upstairs.

Back in the withdrawing room Peggy, Peter and Ruth did their best to placate the indignant Uncle Henry; but it was to no avail. Tight-lipped, the fuming poet and his equally indignant wife strode from the room. They were met in the hallway by Emma and Edward descending the stairs.

"Henry, dear friend, you're not going?" Edward held up his hands in supplication.

"I have been dreadfully humiliated, nay, mortified", cried Henry as he took his coat from the hall-stand. "I shall not lightly undertake to give another recitation in this household under any pretext whatsoever. I may say that for young gentlemen who are scholars at such excellent establishments, I am not a little surprised at such bad behaviour".

He put on his hat and waited for his wife to complete her donning of outdoor clothes. Harriet looked the picture of misery and embarrassment as she stood by her husband's side. Emma tried to plead with them but Henry had already flung open the front door and with "Good night, Edward — Emma" he strode purposefully into the thick heaped snow, down the garden path and turned into their own drive only a few feet away. The front door was banged dramatically behind them.

A somewhat subdued group of parents, aunt and the two remaining rather scared children, surveyed each other, looking extremely miserable in the process.

"A most unfortunate happening, my dear. Now I shall have the unenviable task of trying to smooth ruffled feathers tomorrow", said Edward, as he gathered up music scores from the piano top.

They busied themselves with tidying up the room. Edward doused the lights and damped down the fire. Joining their two eldest in the scullery, he went to the back door, opened it and looked out. The sky had cleared. He could see high in the heavens one star shining very brightly.

A Christmas Star, he said to himself. Let it be a Star of Peace throughout the world. After a few moments he started to shiver, partly with the cold and partly with an inexplicable apprehension. Telling himself not to be foolish he closed and locked the door. The others had all gone up to bed. Slowly and thoughtfully he climbed the stairs to join Emma in their bedroom

As he closed the door the strange disturbing apprehension left him. A peaceful blessed silence descended on the entire house. In two hours it would be Christmas Day.

Christmas Day Dawns

I N 1922 the practice of spending Christmas away from home was very much the exception rather than the rule. It was virtually certain that no one ever dreamed of going abroad to soak up the sun at the festive season, even if they could afford it.

In Wembley Hill the Learner family, broadly speaking, celebrated Christmas Day and Boxing Day in a manner similar to the Joneses, say, in Mostyn Avenue or the Robinsons in Dagmar Avenue. Naturally three or four children in the household made a difference in the degree of enjoyment rejoiced in by individual families. But in the early 1920s large families were very much in vogue. One thing every family, with or without children, enjoyed during this season was a happy, contented, joyous, God-fearing respite from the trials and worries of the workaday world.

Two young Learners, at six o'clock in the morning on the day after their disgrace the night before, had one thing very much in common. They were determined to enjoy to the full this most exciting wonderfully glorious Christmas Day.

"Light the candles John, so's we can see what's in our stockings", cried a breathlessly excited Jim. John clambered over the huge double bed with brass posts and railings at each end to reach the two candles standing like sentinels at both ends of the mantelpiece. Striking a match and hitching up the trouser part of his woollen pyjamas John lit the candles.

The feeble light revealed two bulky Christmas stockings hanging from the horizontal railing at each end of the bed. They were white open-weave canvas stockings, more like long socks, originally flat but now bulging with a variety of exciting objects. Jim had not wasted time and together they exclaimed over the wonderful generosity of a kindly Father Christmas.

They were both still at an age when they truly believed that a dear old gentleman with a white beard and wearing a red coat had clambered down their chimney in the dead of night and planted desirable toys and other thrilling objects in stockings placed overnight at the foot of their bed.

Jim gasped with excitement as he pulled out a model of a Hornby railway engine, a diminutive copy of The Water Babies, a bazooka, a rectangular white India rubber and a blue Sovereign pencil. Right at the bottom of the stocking was a large polished orange.

John showed unbounded delight as a magnifying glass, a fountain pen, a liquorice pipe with red 'hundreds and thousands' depicting a glowing bowl and an exact replica of the orange in Jim's stocking, came into view. They noisily exchanged remarks on their respective good fortune and John said: "I wonder if he's put anything in the bed-posts."

"Coo, yes, let's have a look", said Jim as he scrambled over the bed-cover on his knees to the foot of the bed. Their double bed was of ancient and solid construction with brass uprights placed at six inch intervals. At each corner the hollow uprights were some four inches in diameter. On top of each upright a brass ball was screwed into the inside of the post.

The two youngest Learners for as long as they could remember had scribbled secret messages to each other which they did not want other eyes to see. They fondly believed that they alone were the only two to know that when the brass balls were unscrewed exciting caverns were revealed. But of course, they acknowledged that Father Christmas was all seeing and all knowing. Each of them hastily unscrewed the two brass balls at the foot of the bed. In each cavern a solid object some three inches across wrapped in silver paper was lifted out by eager hands. Feverishly tearing off the wrapping the two lads eyed the contents with unbelieving wonderment.

"What a whopper!" exclaimed Jim holding up his prize to show

John. "Whatever is it? Is it a coin of some sort?" John had been a few seconds behind his quicker brother but now he too examined an identical object to the one Jim held out.

"Well of course it's a coin, you daft thing. Don't you know a crown when you see one?" John asked pretending to be very superior in his worldly knowledge and thinking of all the heavenly things he could buy with this fortune nestling in his hand.

Jim, also, gazed at the treasure he was grasping. Their reverie was interrupted by a loud knocking on the door. Mrs. Learner, in her dressing-gown, poked her head into the room, and told her sons to wash and dress quickly.

* * * *

It was a tradition in the Learner household on Christmas Day for the whole family to descend to the withdrawing room en masse; rather like first footings in the New Year. Excited beyond all bounds the boys finished their ablutions in double quick time, threw on their clothes and opened the bedroom door. Needless to say they were the first on the landing.

In a few moments they were joined by Ruth and their aunt, both in their Sunday best, Ruth looked really nice for once for her aunt to see, whilst Peggy was particularly gay-looking in a flowered woollen dress with a suitably coloured bandeau round her hair to complete the ensemble.

As Merry Christmases were exchanged Peter emerged from his room and the happy salutations were repeated. Then the head of the household poked his head out of his bedroom door, and emitted a boyish 'coo-ee'. On Sundays Edward was invariably impeccably turned out. For this very special day he sported a smart light grey worsted suit which incorporated a five button waistcoat. He had a heavy watch-chain spread from pocket to pocket, a higher than ever choker collar and a large pearl pin inserted in a slightly darker grey cravat.

He received a whacking kiss from his sister and then fondly embraced each of his dear children in turn, wishing them 'Merry Christmas'. Peter was told to call mother up from the kitchen and this done they cavorted merrily up and down on the landing accompanied by shrieks of laughter from aunt and children alike.

Mrs. Learner hastened upstairs, exchanged greetings with everyone and disappeared into the bedroom to reappear in a few moments tastefully attired in a purple taffetta moire silk ankle-length dress. Peter was nicely dressed in his best school blazer, grey trousers with a good crease in them and well polished black shoes. Christmas came but once a year. Each and every one of them wanted to look his or her best.

Father led the procession downstairs followed by the rest of the family in a state of unbridled excitement and waiting outside the withdrawing room for all to assemble, opened the door with a flourish.

Cries of wonderment fell from half a dozen lips. They were amazed to see the transformation from the way the room looked the night before. Edward's voice was heard above all the hullaballoo: "Right, children, that's it. Jim, leave that parcel alone, you know the rules. No presents until after breakfast".

"After breakfast all these presents and parcels will be taken up to one of the boys' bedrooms for distribution", Emma explained to Peggy. Peggy nodded; this was her first initiation into the Learner family's Christmas traditions.

It was still dark as they all trooped into a gas-lit kitchen for breakfast. The curtains were closely drawn and the room was as cosy as Emma's efforts had made it. The usual homely warmth from the extra specially black-leaded range ensured the comforts of the room's occupants. A breakfast of porridge, boiled eggs, bread and butter liberally spread with honey or marmalade and piping hot tea poured from a vast family heirloom teapot was hungrily despatched by the Learner brood, then all repaired to Jim and John's bedroom. The next event in family tradition was about to take place.

A Near-tragedy

FOR the past three or four years a novel manner of distributing the Christmas presents had been introduced by Edward Learner. The idea was for each male member of the family to take it in turns to dress up as Father Christmas, supervise the assembly of all the presents in a central place and hand them out to the relevant recipients.

Edward himself performed the initial ceremony and by 1922 the turn had come round to John. An ancient dark red dressing-gown was put on, the beard was shaped out of cotton wool and a hood trimmed with whitish fur was loaned by a reluctant mum.

John duly donned these garments (all much too big for him) on this particular festive day and looked rather like a waif or a stray in from the cold. When he put on the hood his face was practically hidden from view. As for the beard, no amount of manoeuvering would keep it in the correct place. Jim was hysterical with laughter as poor John made his entrance, fiddling with the beard and trying to apologise to Aunt Peggy in muffled terms.

John had decided to stack the presents in the wardrobe in their bedroom. With dad's help the entire contents of the ancient and venerable clothes cupboard had been removed. The wardrobe itself was taller than the usual run of such items of furniture. A drawer normally used to accommodate woollen blankets, running the whole length of the closet was positioned underneath as an integral part of the body of the piece of furniture. At this time of the year with blankets being much in use the drawer was empty. Infrequently used suit-cases were stacked on top and inevitably attracted the dust. Finally, a long glass mirror some six feet long and eighteen inches wide was fixed to the door of the wardrobe.

All in the room were about to witness John becoming the innocent victim of a near tragedy. Watched by six pairs of eyes whose owners were in various states of excitement, he climbed into the wardrobe and almost closed the door. Immediately he opened the door again and gave a very good imitation of Father Christmas. "Ho. Ho. Ho." But he was too quick and eager to exercise caution.

The wardrobe teetered on its base. A shout of warning from father was accompanied by frantic cries from other lips. John tried desperately to hold on to the sides of the doorway. But the whole thing shook with a terrifying to-ing and fro-ing motion, until it fell with a sickening crash onto the brass railings of the bed. Glass was scattered all over the bed and on the bedroom linoleum.

Poor John was catapulted on to the ground at the foot of the bedstead where he lay inert. Frantic action from all sides was immediate. "Come on, old boy", said a distraught Edward, "I'm here, son, I'm here". He shoved aside the pile of presents which had been thrown onto the floor and lifted John up in his strong arms. "Peter open our bedroom door, we'll lay him on our bed".

Peter ran out as Aunt Peggy tried to comfort little Jim who was terribly scared by the crash and was sobbing with fright. Ruth, also, was very scared but put on a brave face and held on to John's hand as he was carried out of the room. The whole place looked as if it had been hit by an earthquake. Some of the glass which had landed on the floor was trodden with a dreadful scrunching noise into the linoleum. The wardrobe lay on its front with the door hanging at an angle on one hinge. The bed had been partly pushed aside with the force of the fall.

Jim tore himself away from his aunt, ran out of the room and stood outside his parents' bedroom straining to hear a sound or something to tell him John was not dead.

Poor Aunt Peggy, a sad witness of this dreadful happening, moved disconsolately round the room picking up the presents, some with their wrappings torn off in the fall. She ran downstairs to fetch dustpan and brush.

Edward and Emma, in their bedroom, bent anxiously over the body of their beloved son. The colour was mercifully beginning to return to his cheeks; his lips were moving, and he was regaining consciousness. His eyes opened and he looked round at the strange surroundings.

"It's all right, John darling, mummy's here, you're going to be all right". She kissed his wet cheeks. She could see a nasty swelling had begun to appear on the poor boy's forehead where he had knocked himself on the base of the bed in falling.

In a little while he was able, with his father's help, to struggle to his feet. He looked down at himself and grinned faintly at his parents when he realised he was still wearing the red dressing-gown.

Emma led John down to the kitchen where he was sat in front of the range and given a glass of warm milk. After bathing his forehead she told Ruth to stay with him and rushed upstairs again to help Edward and Peggy put the bedroom to rights. In the meantime Peter and Jim had been instructed to take all the presents downstairs again to the withdrawing room. The three adults had been forced to shake all the broken glass from the bed on to the floor. It was a dreadful mess.

"I shall have to take the whole bed apart, sheets, blankets, coverlet, all the lot", said a distraught Emma, "before we can let them sleep in the bed again".

She was amazed to see that Edward and Peggy, between them, had managed to push the wardrobe back against the wall. Edward had fetched a screwdriver and removed the other door hinge. He had to struggle hard to lift the door off and prop it against a wall without loosening any more glass. Within half an hour the room had been more or less put to rights. Peter and Jim came back into the bedroom.

"We'll all say a prayer together in thankfulness to Our Lord for sparing my dear son from what could have been a terrible fate" said Edward. Looking round at all the others in the bedroom, he got down on his knees. Edward, Aunt Peggy, Peter and Jim followed suit. After the prayer he suggested everyone get ready for church.

* * * *

Mercifully the service was quite short with the family's favourite carol, 'Christians Awake', being sung lustily by a large congregation. Mr. Blakey's sermon lasted only twenty minutes instead of the normal, seemingly endless half hour. The organist was in his element as he blasted out the accompaniment to the last carol, 'Hark the Herald Angels sing'.

Going home again via Park Lane they climbed the steep path to the top of Linden Avenue. At the top the children slipped and slid all the way down the hill towards home, to be greeted with the mouth-watering aroma of turkey and trimmings.

* * * *

"Dinner ready in fifteen minutes", a voice called from the depth of the kitchen, "everybody ready by then, I don't want the meal to be spoiled".

This was the signal for everyone to bustle about. Well before the fifteen minutes had elapsed they were all, with the exception of mum and dad, seated round the dining-room table. Aunt Peggy was dressed in yet another attractive creation, a crimson silk dress with a long necklace of ivory beads, ivory ear-rings to match and her hair drawn back into twin coils on the nape of her neck. She looked radiant. John and the others kept giving her admiring looks.

Even though a little daylight could penetrate the gloom of the room the gas mantles had been lit. A cheerful fire burned in the grate. Right on time the head of the household entered the dining-room carrying a huge platter, nearly staggering with the weight of the magnificent bird, plump and roasted brown, covering the entire base of the beautiful willow pattern china dish. Rousing cheers greeted the sight of such a succulent looking turkey.

Mother followed him carrying a large tray with four identical willow pattern vegetable dishes. Two gravy boats with covers (also bearing the well known willow pattern) had already been placed on the sideboard and there were two more receptacles filled to the brim with bread sauce and stuffing. Jim's eyes nearly popped out of their sockets as he gazed at the sight of all this wonderful fare.

This was not surprising. In previous years a large chicken was the ultimate treat for the special day. And to the children a chicken was something special. When one or the other of them went down with influenza or a similar complaint, a small portion of chicken followed by a dose of quinine or cod liver oil or extract of malt was given them to aid their recovery. Chicken was, to them, a real treat to be savoured sparingly.

But this Christmas Emma, with her husband's complete agreement, and in view of the honoured guest, had decided that a turkey would be more suitable and much more enjoyabe. This decision had met with everyone's approval.

When all plates were filled with substantial helpings of the festive fare, father bowed his head, waited for his family to follow suit and said Grace. Then the serious business of consuming the massed turkey and trimmings on each plate got well under way.

"Congratulations, mother, you've certainly lived up to your reputation of being the best cook in the district". said Edward when everyone had finished and the dishes and plates were cleared to await the arrival of the Christmas pudding.

Emma was a very good cook. She had made sure that although they had all (except her husband) helped with the stirring of the pudding, she was only satisfied with the consistency of the mix after giving it another vigorous mixing herself. Four large sized pudding basins were filled with the stirred ingredients, each basin was wrapped in flannelette and the material was tied at the top in a secure knot.

These were then placed in a huge blackened cooking pot (rather like a Dixie in the boys' Scout camp) and slowly boiled for approximately four hours. The smell from the kitchen range had driven the children, up in their bedrooms, wild with delight.

As one of the puddings was now placed in the middle of the table with a sprig of holly stuck in the top, more loud cheers and energetic hand clapping greeted its appearance. Substantial portions were dolloped on to each dessert plate and hot thick custard was poured over the delicious looking, almost black, pudding. (Brandy was absolutely forbidden; apart from Emma's milk stout alcohol was barred from Letchworth).

Jim did not waste any time. Delving into the delectable dark rich portion on his plate, he searched frantically for a threepenny bit.

"Oh, it's not fair, there's no threepenny bit in my portion", he said with a miserable expression on his face.

"Never mind, my boy", said his father, "you can have this one". He passed a coin covered with pudding over to Jim. "I've found two in mine".

Edward beamed at his wife fondly with his mouth full of food – a thing he would have frowned upon in his children at other times. "Your Christmas puddings seem to get better every year".

Aunt Peggy nodded. She was overwhelmed with the quality and quantity of the feast and the wonderful kindness of every soul gathered round the board. Sitting happily with these dear people she knew she would always remember this particular Christmas. But she could not possibly have had any idea of the momentous events to come which were to make it even more memorable.

Tea and More Disaster

CHRISTMAS dinner was voted a huge success by each and every member of the Learner family. Edward had looked round at all the happy faces obviously entirely absorbed with the good things he himself had been able to provide. Once again he thanked God that the hospital order for overalls had come in time for all this to be possible.

Shortly after the meal when all hands were busy at the pumps (i.e. the kitchen sink), Jim told his mother he didn't feel too well. Emma looked at him and said: "I'm not surprised the way you put away all that rich Christmas pudding. You'll be as right as rain in an hour or two". She watched him as he slowly and laboriously wiped a dinner plate.

The washing-up finally completed, Aunt Peggy, Emma and Ruth took off their aprons and joined in the procession to the withdrawing room. John, back in his Master of Ceremonies dark red dressing-gown, was allowed to be in the lead. Even with all the dramatic happenings which had taken place in the last few hours, they were all mightily excited and buoyed up at the prospect of giving and accepting Christmas presents.

John made a bee-line for the biggest parcel nestling at the foot of the attractive tree. 'To Daddy from Emma' John read out, and handed the parcel to a smiling Edward. As he fumbled with the string and wrapping he would not let on by so much as a smirk that he already knew what the parcel contained.

"Oh, I say — Good heavens! — Good gracious! — just look at this beautiful cardigan, just what I've always wanted". He held up the grey cable stitch woollen cardigan in front of him for all to see. "Mother, this is going to be much appreciated in this weather". He gave his wife a kiss.

Loud laughter greeted the sight of Emma giving a handsome knitted scarf to Peggy only to receive the next moment an almost identical hand-knitted scarf from her sister-in-law. They made a play of handing back their scarves to each other.

Jim was beside himself with joy at opening a present from his beloved aunt. She had given him a Meccano Set No. 10A – the very latest model. He had been looking at the very same thing at the toy shop in the High Road only a few days ago and had been hoping against hope that Father Christmas would bring him one. There was a cry of delight as John held up a present from his dad. "Look what I've got – a compass, and all the points of the compass are in red; coo, thanks daddy, wait till I show it to all my pals in my scout patrol". Aunt Peggy was obviously overjoyed with the real leather music case given by her brother. All eyes were turned to Emma when she gave a gasp of delight for Edward had bought her a most magnificent silver pendant watch suspended on a black moire silk ribbon.

The final gift had been given out and even with all the little bits and bobs and coloured balls on the tree, it now looked sadly bare and neglected. John was relieved to be able to take off his Father Christmas outfit; his head was aching and he had been getting rather warm. Edward, now temporarily attired in his lovely new cardigan said he thought it would be a good idea if the presents were put aside for the time being. "Anybody who wants to can accompany me for a bit of a walk to help get the Christmas dinner down".

"That's a very good idea", said Emma, "but of course I shan't be able to go; I've got to get the tea ready".

"Come on, everybody set to", Edward said in a business-like manner, but they didn't get far. There were two things against a long walk right now. Snow was falling heavily again and his sister complained of the cold. Going as far as half way down Raglan Gardens they decided that was enough and returned home with time to spare before high tea at 5 o'clock.

* * * *

Margaret Caroline Learner could hardly believe her eyes. As she entered the dining-room the sight which met her astonished gaze literally took her breath away.

What a spread! Emma, however did you manage to prepare all this..." She waved her hand over the attractively-laid table. Ruth and the three boys following her in shouted with unbridled joy at the wonderful spectacle.

The dining-room presented the same picture of cosy warmth and bonhomie as it did at dinner time. But now the heavy curtains were drawn, all gas mantles were lit and the oil lamp, filled to the brim with paraffin oil and wick carefully trimmed, stood burning brightly on the sideboard. A small coal fire was burning in the grate; small was the operative word, Edward knew the room would soon be too hot with seven individuals seated round the table.

The dining-room table with pure white damask cloth spread over the entire surface was laid out in a manner which almost defied description. Every place had its own dinner plate, side plate, two knives, fork and two spoons, best double damask serviette in individual serviette ring, crystal glass tumbler and cup and saucer. On every available space in the centre of the table were plates of sliced turkey, ham, tongue, cold beetroots, potatoes, hard boiled eggs and home made salad dressing.

There were serving spoons in profusion, two enormous cut glass water jugs and on each side plate was placed a brightly coloured Christmas cracker. The table had been so exactly meticulously laid there was not an inch of space for so much as an egg-cup. On the sideboard and on a small card table brought in for the purpose there were cut glass bowls containing trifles, stewed fruits, cream and two or three different coloured jellies. Two large home-made loaves on bread boards decorated with harvest corn sheaves and two dishes of butter fashioned in little rolls completed the feast.

Later at the sight of Emma's magnificent cake, resplendent with icing, marzipan, sprigs of holly, two little very red-breasted robins and a remarkably cheerful looking Father Christmas being triumphantly borne into the room, there were resounding cheers. A place was cleared in the centre of the table, the handsome cake knife was placed ready for action and father was about to do his duty. But he was stopped by Emma who said it would be much better if we all waited a bit while the tea was being made.

"A good idea, mother, and while we are waiting perhaps we can after all pull the crackers now, eh, Jim?"

Gaily coloured paper hats were donned and everybody wanted to read out his motto at the same time. Peter grinned as he said: "Listen everybody, here's a corker:-

'There's a breed of dog in Tibet born with no nose' 'Really? How do they smell?' 'AWFUL'

Groans and laughter. It was Jim's turn. He chuckled so much his aunt said she couldn't catch what he was saying. He tried again:-

"'Schoolmaster to pupil: what's a polygon, Jones?' 'Please sir, a dead parrot'"

More laughter.

"Listen to this one, everybody". All heads turned to father.

"What was the elephant doing when he sent a message from one side of the forest to the other?" Edward looked up. Nobody answered. "He was making a trunk call".

Emma came in bearing a family heirloom — a magnificent teapot decorated with various coloured exotic flowers. It would have been truer to say that Emma staggered in; the teapot looked as if it contained enough tea to feed an army. It was put on the sideboard and after she had pulled her cracker and donned a funny hat, she proceeded to pour tea into the cups duly passed to her by all and sundry.

"Edward, move the lamp on to the table, there's plenty of room now and we shall be able to see the cake all the better". Ruth and Aunt Peggy moved aside as the lamp was carefully placed close to the wonderful Christmas cake.

Edward picked up the cake knife. He loved to see his children laughing and enjoying themselves and, with this in mind, he made a play at slicing at a non-existent cake in mid air — rather in the manner of a conductor leading his orchestra. Jim and John nearly went into hysterics watching him. On a sideways movement of his hand, however, he caught the tall glass funnel of the oil- lamp a resounding blow; and it fell smack into the middle of the beautiful cake, the oil pouring out all over the top of it.

There was consternation in the room, the happy laughter turning suddenly into screams and wails. Mercifully the flame on the wick was doused and Mr. Learner tried desperately to stem the progress of the oil some of which had run across the table-cloth and on to Peggy's lap. Mrs. Learner shouted for everbody to get up from their chairs. She grabbed one of her best damask serviettes and tried, ineffectively, to soak up oil which had got past her husband's efforts. The cake was ruined; it would be absolutely uneatable.

Everyone set to clearing everything from the table and on to the sideboard, and the three boys ran as fast as their legs could carry them into the scullery for every old rag they could lay their hands on. In the meantime Mr. Learner had removed the offending lamp from the centre of the table and carried it, brass base and broken funnel, out into the scullery.

Returning to the dining-room (wiping his hands on a piece of cloth) he gazed woefully at the scene of the room's desolation. He hurriedly smothered the remaining fire in the grate for fear of a further tragedy. Some of the lamp oil had dripped to the floor and was seeping ominously towards the fireplace.

With the shouting and wailing still going on, the ruined tablecloth in a crumpled heap thrown over a chair, a jumble of plates, dishes, serviettes and pulled crackers strewn all over the sideboard and poor Aunt Peggy surveying her oil-soaked dress, it looked for all the world like a horrible nightmare one would suffer after overeating late at night.

Every one of them helped restore some semblance of normality to the situation. The paraffin oil smell was dreadful; it would be days before the smell of the stuff diminished. It was while they were striving to clear up the mess that they heard a knock on the front door. Everyone looked startled.

"Who on earth can that be on Christmas night?" Emma looked at Edward, who hurried along the hallway to the door.

A well-known voice could be heard booming out: "My dear Edward, I've come to offer an olive branch. I said to Harriet I could not let this festive day pass without offering my apologies for my churlish behaviour last night".

Edward, who was always the soul of politeness, had to stem the flow of Henry's sincere apologies. "Henry, my dear chap, it's so good of you to call. I'm afraid I cannot ask you to come in — we've just had a most dreadful upset during our Christmas tea. My dear wife's Christmas cake has been smothered in lamp oil".

Emma put her head round the dining-room door. "Please excuse us, Henry. There's a most awful mess and I'm afraid the house will be reeking of oil. Henry, will you tell Harriet Edward and I will call and see you tomorrow".

Henry retired sorrowfully to his own home. He relayed the sad tidings to his wife and they commiserated with each other over the sufferings of the little family next door.

The Learner family had indeed suffered not one but two near-tragedies on this Christmas Day in 1922. Boxing Day, however, was fated to bring an even more disturbing event into the household.

Jim is Taken to Hospital

*"Mummy! Mummy" Come quickly. Jim says he's feeling
ill". John kept banging and banging on his parents' bedroom
door. He kept on and on — the urgency could be felt like
something tangible.*

"Mummy! Daddy! Open the door quickly!"

OTHER doors were opening as first Peter and then Ruth and
a sleepy Aunt Peggy looked out on the landing. Mr. Learner
appeared candle in hand, which cast a faint patch of light
onto the immediate surroundings. His free hand was quickly seized
by John who pulled him towards his brother's room.

"John, what's the matter? It's half past five in the morning.
You're making enough noise to wake the dead". He could see now
that Peter, Ruth and his sister were crowding round the door.

"It's Jimmy; he keeps swallowing and he's covered in awful red
spots. Come and look at him, Daddy, it's awful".

There were gasps of horror from the others as Edward led the
way, his flickering candle casting a ghostly light as he sped along
the corridor. He strode into Jim's room which was only feebly lit by
a candle on one corner of the mantelpiece.

Holding his candle close to Jim, he could see the poor lad was
obviously in great distress. Every few seconds he tried to swallow as
he lay in bed with his head close up to the bed railings. Sweat was
pouring off him. Edward was horrified to see the whole of Jim's face
and neck were covered in a bright red rash; it was a truly terrifying

sight. He looked back towards the door where the others were standing – obviously reluctant to come into the room – and held up a hand.

"Don't come in any of you. Peter, go and call your mother – she can't have heard any of this commotion".

Peter dashed back along the landing. Edward lifted his son up in the bed and put a pillow behind his head. He tried to comfort him but Jim was unable to speak; he appeared to be delirious. In a few moments Emma came flying along the corridor, dressing-gown only just covering her and hair streaming behind. She pushed her way past the horrified Peggy and Ruth, who were peering into the room, trying hard to glimpse the luckless Jim.

"Edward! What's happened to my little Jimmy? Peter says he's covered in spots". She put her hand on Jim's forehead. "It's burning hot and look at my boy's face and neck". She pulled Jim towards her; she held him close, rocking him to and fro on the bed.

"Is it chicken pox?" asked Mr. Learner. He's so hot and I've never seen such awful livid spots". He turned in complete bewilderment to Emma. Emma stopped rocking the suffering lad and held him at arms' length; she looked at him hard and long.

"Edward – you must go and get Doctor Dyson now – I think it's worse than chicken pox". She took a deep breath. "I think our poor boy has got scarlet fever".

The dread disease was on everybody's lips. Edward lingered no longer; dashing out of the room he prepared himself for the cold, miserable journey to the doctor on a cold, miserable Boxing Day morning. He could not be sure the good doctor, who had attended him and his family for many many years, would even be at home. A telephone at this time would have saved a lot of trouble; there had never been a telephone installed at Letchworth.

To the waiting Emma, Aunt Peggy and all the others, the period whilst Edward was on his errand of mercy seemed an eternity. Peggy helped Emma to tidy up the bed and attempted to make poor Jim as comfortable as possible. He was twisting and turning and throwing off the bed covers in fits of gasping, attempted swallowing and awful moaning.

Ruth flew to and fro from the bathroom with pails of cold water which she poured into the basin on the wash-stand. A flannel dipped in this cold water was repeatedly pressed onto the sweating lad's burning forehead, face and neck. Emma tried hard to be brave, but the tears were coursing down her cheeks. Peter and John stood rooted to the spot still standing by the sick boy's bedroom door.

At last the sound of a key being inserted in the lock made everyone tense. Peter and John raced to the top of the stairs and looked down the well of the stairs to see if the doctor was with their father. Had their father been able to persuade him to turn out at such an inconvenient time? What would his verdict be after he had examined Jim? These and other questions crowded through the minds of each and every one of them.

Doctor Dyson was an old family friend of the Learner's as well as being their physician of many years standing. He was a spruce figure, familiar to all in the district with his doctor's bag and was well-known for his kindliness and excellent bedside manner.

Racing up the stairs now with Edward in close pursuit, he ordered everybody except Jim's parents to leave the bedroom clear. Emma drew in her breath sharply as the doctor removed Jim's pyjama jacket. The red rash had completely covered his chest.

"Is it — is it scarlet fever, Doctor?" she said. She shuddered and instinctively groped for her husband's hand as the doctor nodded emphatically.

"No doubt at all I'm afraid, poor lad. He will have to be sent immediately to the Isolation Hospital in Wales Farm Road in Acton; he'll probably be there for at least six weeks. "

"And not only that", he went on. "The whole house will have to be fumigated from top to bottom. There'll be no school for your other children when they're due back there — the risk of infection during the period of incubation is very very serious — and you yourselves should be confined to the house as much as possible".

He addressed his next remark to Emma: "Try not to get too close to whoever's serving you at the shops".

"Doctor, what about my business? My livelihood? I shall have to go to work..." Edward paused "What can I do? What do you suggest?"

"I can't order you not to leave this house, my dear old friend, I can only advise you to be in contact with other people as little as possible. We don't want an epidemic on our hands, do we?"

Edward looked absolutely lost as he digested this rhetorical question. Emma suddenly said: "Oh, Doctor, my sister-in-law is staying with us over Christmas. She lives in Redhill in Surrey and was going home next week-end. Can she go home, Doctor?"

The doctor hesitated. He stroked his chin and said firmly: "I would not recommend for one moment that she should return to the bosom of her family. The risk of infection is too great. No — I'm afraid she'll have to remain as your guest for the period of Jim's illness". He started towards the door; within a few moments he was gone.

With the doctor's departure Edward called the family together downstairs in the kitchen. He told Peggy and the others exactly what the doctor had said, stressing the seriousness of the situation.

Aunt Peggy's face was a study. She was torn between the joy of an enforced stay with her dear brother and his family, and the realisation that her situation was going to be very awkward. She had a long-standing engagement to play a piano solo at a local concert in the first week of the New Year. However, being a sensible individual she knew she had no option. She smiled understandingly at Edward.

* * * *

It was no more than threequarters of an hour since the departure of Doctor Dyson when there was a loud rat-a-tat on the front door. Peter opened it and was confronted by a mountain of a man wearing a khaki overall and with a mask covring his mouth and nose.

"Is this the Learner house, young feller-me-lad?"

"Ye-es, it is, that's right", said a startled Peter. He looked beyond the huge man and saw a grey motorised van with a red cross painted on its side parked right outside the house. The rest of the family had now joined Peter at the door.

"Morning, sir, we received a telephone call from a Doctor Dyson to collect a young person by the name of James Learner. I've been instructed to take him to the Acton Isolation Hospital without delay".

They entered the boys' bedroom and the ambulanceman wrapped a blanket round Jim, lifting him bodily from the bed. Jim was no lightweight but the man handled him as though he was just a feather.

Ruth and all the others watched in complete silence as the man walked through the already-opened front door, stepped carefully over the iced-over pathway, got into the passenger seat of the waiting ambulance, settled Jim onto his lap and was driven away down the hill by his colleague. The last thing they remember seeing was the scared face of poor young Jim looking at them out of the window. He seemed to be saying: "What a rotten way to end Christmas".

New Year of Change

L IFE for Mr. and Mrs. Learner, their progeny and their guest continued sombrely and unhappily in the first few months of the New Year. They visited the hospital frequently. Jim's temperature continued to give concern to the hospital ward doctor and the ugly rash remained on the upper part of his torso. Mr. Learner was told at a later date that Jim's condition had been extremely critical but, gradually, due to his normally healthy constitution, and the efforts of the hospital staff, he slowly and painfully recovered.

The ward in which Jim was a patient had large windows looking out onto a rather drab snow-covered court-yard. On the occasions of his parents' visits he was naturally not allowed to come into contact with them. Instead the poor lad had to be content with mouthing various little messages through a firmly-closed window.

Apart from reading copies of his 'Magnet' brought to him, he spent most of the long days eating, sleeping and looking round the ward. A young man in the bed opposite tried to keep him amused with jokes and facial contortions. At night when the lights were lowered he made Jim quite sad by singing:

"I only have one sweetheart in the whole wide world,

"And that's my dear old mother".

However on a glorious day almost exactly six weeks from the day he entered hospital, he was told he would be going home; the rash had gone and he was almost his old self again. Saying his farewells to the nursing staff, particularly to a sweet little nurse who had given him a bath and with whom he fell quite in love, he awaited the arrival of his mother with mounting excitement.

The sun was shining as they boarded a tram to take them back to Wembley Hill. Emma asked him if he would like a special treat to celebrate his home-coming, and Jim's answer was to drag her into Aldridge's and point out his favourite mouth-watering cake provocatively displayed on one of the shelves.

Arriving home to a house which seemed to Jim not a little strange after his sojourn in hospital, he was surrounded by the jovial back-slapping and leg-pulling of his brothers and sister. His happiness was somewhat muted by the absence of his dear Aunt Peggy who, he was told, had gone home a few days ago.

He very soon returned to the regularity of life in his own home. Dad said he and the others would be going back to school on Monday of next week. His mother reminded him that he must now settle down to writing his 'thankyou' letters to all his relatives who had remembered him at Christmas time. A job Jim very definitely hated doing. When asked later on if he had finished them he replied: "Oh, yes, twice!"

Back to the joys of playing in the garden, making mud pies, looking through all his favourite boys' magazines, listening in to the crystal set and getting back to the routine of normal, everyday life, Jim and the others, were glad to return to a comfortable lifestyle at Letchworth. But in Wembley Hill in 1923 events were taking place which were to change dramatically the 'modus vivendi' of the Learner family.

* * * *

Edward Learner read the local newspaper from cover to cover every Saturday evening after his post prandial nap. On this particular Saturday he lowered his paper, looked at his wife busy doing mending and at the children who were either playing with cigarette cards, reading magazines or drawing, and cleared his throat.

In a manner which they knew foretold an important announcement he said: "Well, my dear, and children, it looks as if our quiet, peaceful Wembley Hill is going to be invaded".

"Invaded!", cried John, "D'you mean the Germans have landed and we're going to be attacked?" His eyes lit up with excitement. Ruth looked quite alarmed.

Edward chuckled. He got up from his chair and crossed over to the fireplace. "I'm sorry, dears, I shouldn't have used quite such a dramatic turn of phrase. But I've just been reading in the paper that Wembley has finally been chosen as the site of a sports stadium and..." he emphasised the next few words "...of the British Empire Exhibition."

The children momentarily stopped their activities, attempting to digest what their father had just told them.

Peter asked: "Will the sports stadium be a big affair, father? I mean, what sort of sports will take place there. For instance, will there be a cricket pitch?"

"I expect it will be quite big, my son. I don't know about cricket but I should think there'll probably be football and rugger amongst other things".

"And what will happen at a British Empire Exhibition?" Ruth wanted to know.

"Well, darling, I don't know but I should imagine that some of the countries in our Empire will be showing their products in a large building. I expect it will take quite a few months to get it ready".

Their father's announcement continued to cause a good deal of interest to them all. After a spate of further questions and guess-work answers the subject was brought to a close. Father said he had some work to do in the dining-room and he was going to smoke a cigarette.

It was only a few days after he had read the report of the imminent events in the environs of Wembley that life began to be markedly different for the Learner children.

Empire Stadium Takes Shape

MOST of the snow had gone in early March, but the weather continued to be cold and windy. Spring was very reluctant to show its hand but folk were glad to know that winter was losing its grip at last.

Going about their business in Wembley Hill the shoppers, tradesmen and local people noticed a definite change in the volume of traffic using Wembley Hill Road. Heavy lorries loaded with earth and gravel ran up and down between the High Road and a new road almost opposite the end of Linden Avenue.

The unaccustomed noise was equally exciting to the youth of the district as it was upsetting to most of the local shop-keepers. Clods of mud and heaps of gravel were deposited in the road and this was inevitably brought into their premises on the feet of their patrons.

This new road led up to a vast site on the actual spot in Wembley Park where Watkin's Folly had stood since its inception in 1893. The tower, which had been dubbed Watkin's Folly because it had never been properly costed and was never finished, was open to the public from 1893 until 1902. Amongst other unsatisfactory elements of its unsafe design was the dangerous condition of the lift machinery. The lift had originally taken visitors up to a height of 155 feet, but because of neglect the machinery was declared unsafe.

The contract to demolish the unfinished tower was given to Messrs. Heenan and Stroude who had to suffer the ignominy of demolishing the structure they had built. The final explosives used to complete the demolition were placed in position in September 1907.

It was on a field adjacent to this very site where the Learner children frequently played games and took their picnic lunches. The use of this lovely field, strewn with buttercups, daisies and meadowsweet, which had given them such glorious youthful happiness for so long, was to be denied them for evermore. For on the actual site of Watkin's Folly the foundations of the Wembley Stadium were firmly and inexorably sunk.

Great lorries loaded with cement shed their liquid cargo almost — but not quite! — on the doorsteps of Linden Avenue and Dagmar Avenue. John and Jim, always first home from school, watched with wide-eyed amazement as these lorries rumbled slowly and noisily along Wembley Hill Road. With their mouths hanging open they watched as a ten foot high concrete wall with strange window-like apertures dotted along its considerable length was speedily constructed.

They gaped as they could see several concrete aisles or lanes being laid down between the concrete wall and Wembley Hill Road. They were not long in discovering that the apertures in the wall were for the use of clerks to be employed in due course. Their job would be to issue tickets to members of the public visiting the stadium.

And the lanes in front of the main entrance to the Wembley Stadium were for fleets of buses to disgorge their passengers, all anxious and eager to visit the widely-publicised stadium.

All the local children discovered to their joy that these very handy bus lanes were ready made for indulging in the grand sport of roller-skating. Sweeping up and down the lanes when there were no buses about, Ruth, John and Jim were adept at this sport. They made their mother quite angry when she noticed the sides of their boot soles developed small clefts. The skates they wore had metal clips which fixed into the front of the boots and were fastened by leather straps passing over the instep. When these clefts became splits in the sole she insisted that small additional straps should be worn around the front of the foot.

Peter never took to roller-skating. Not before the advent of the stadium and not now. He spent any spare time he had, which was very little as he was studying hard for his matriculation examination, walking up to the site of the Empire Stadium. He was frequently told by the site engineer to 'clear off out of it'. But from his observations he was able to report exciting developments to the family.

"It's going to be the most colossal building I've ever seen", he told them. "They're excavating tons and tons of clay soil from the hill on which that old tower stood. That's to make a great bowl for the arena of the stadium. And there are going to be twin-rounded towers or domes at each end of the building which will be a landmark for miles and miles around".

He was terribly excited about the whole thing. John and Jim hung on to his every word. Ruth was not interested in how the stadium was being built; she bemoaned the fact that the horses being used to transport building supplies to the sites were being made to haul far too heavy loads.

Work on the stadium continued throughout March and April. Mr. Learner read out to his assembled family in the dining-room a report from the local newspaper:-

The strength of the floors of this remarkable Empire Stadium is being tested by the application of heavy sand on its surfaces. A battalion of 1,200 men are to be marched about the stadium in close formation. They will stand and sit in unison, they will mark time in step and they will be ordered to sway and surge upon the barriers. The assumption is being made that the stadium will be hypothetically able to carry a far greater number of spectators than it is originaly designed to hold. This will be finally tested in the extreme situation of the 1923 Football Cup Final.

Events would show how greatly the volume of spectators at the first ever Wembley Cup Final would put these preparations to an inordinately severe test.

* * * *

On his way to Oakington Avenue, where Jim attended a small but

143

select private school of five pupils run by a governess, he had the choice of walking along Manor Drive or down Raglan Gardens. They both emerged into different parts of Wembley Park Drive. Each choice had, in normal times, its own fascination.

Going via Manor Drive Jim loved looking at the front gardens and into the front windows of the fifty or sixty houses and bungalows he passed en route. Being of a friendly disposition he frequently stopped to talk to someone working in the garden or just coming out of his front door. He knew each one of the three or four houses where a sleepy cat dozed happily on its individual garden wall.

He loved cats; it was not unknown for him to arrive late at school, explaining to the patiently waiting Miss Henderson that he 'couldn't resist stroking Smokey'.

On the other hand he was equally fascinated with the exciting adventures he encountered on the derelict land down one side of Raglan Gardens. Originally covered with lush grass in its heydey, the sizeable stretch of open land from Wembley Hill Road to the junction with Wembley Park Drive was now a jumble of bits of wood, broken glass jars, scraps of paper and other odds and ends of rubbish.

Jim was drawn from the gravel footpath to the derelict open ground as if by a strong magnet. He was searching for treasure trove. His mother scolded him time and time again about the state of his boots. Driven to a fury when she discovered that the toe of one boot was worn right through, she elicited the tearful story from him that he was 'dribbling' as he looked for more sixpences.

It transpired that on one memorable occasion he unearthed two sixpences lying close together under what had once been somebody's handkerchief. Thereafter young Jim had remained forever hopeful of further exciting finds.

The magical attraction of the left hand side of Raglan Gardens was now switched to the mind-boggling happenings on the right hand side. In future Jim definitely decided his route to the school, and during all his hours of playtime, would be devoted to the Raglan Garden route where he could watch strange buildings springing up on huge areas of land on the old Wembley Park pleasure gardens.

The whole of this triangular area bounded on one side by the Metropolitan Railway, on one side by the L.N.E.R. line and on the third side by Wembley Hill Road, had been fenced off and in no time at all it became a concrete jungle.

The Learner family were well aware of the advent of the British Empire Exhibition. The skeletons of the various buildings now being speedily erected would, on completion, soon be internationally known as the Palace of Arts, The Palace of Engineering and the Palace of Industry, etc., to name but a few.

Further afield, too far away for Jim and his family to be able to see, a multiplicity of even stranger edifices sprang up almost overnight. Pavilions soon to contain indigenous products of New Zealand, Australia, India, Bermuda, Canada, Fiji, East Africa and many others were taking shape.

The tremendous speed at which the entire area of 216 acres became filled with buildings of all shapes and sizes was due in no small part to the fact that nearly 2000 men were busy in their construction. Mr. Learner expressed his whole-hearted approval, in association with many other local residents, that the majority of the work was being carried out by men who had served their country during the Great War.

The work on this vast site was scheduled for completion in time for the official opening of the exhibition some time in 1924. Regrettably, due to industrial action, all the buildings had not been completed by the time the exhibition was formally opened by King George V on Saint George's Day, 23rd April, 1924.

BOOK 3

Cup Final Fever

Emma Learner called her offspring into the kitchen and waited until they were all seated round the table. A feeling of intense excitement and expectation permeated the room on this very special day, for the first Football Cup Final was to be played in the brand new Wembley Empire Stadium.

Peter, who had already shown his superior knowledge of the game by forecasting that West Ham would easily beat Bolton Wanderers by a wide margin was on edge with excitement. When his father came back from the factory at noon, they were all going to have an early dinner and then he and his Father would join the huge throng of people all jostling to pass through the turnstiles and make the historic journey to the stadium entrance.

He was going to be one of the lucky people to sit in that vast stadium — which he had watched take shape brick by brick, section by section, for many months — and cheer his favourite team to the echo.

Even in the comparative quietness of their own kitchen the sounds of shouting, excited expectant crowds, the roar of buses, char-a- bancs, taxis, motor cars and other vehicles and the general atmosphere of a nation bent upon enjoying itself, infiltrated the walls of the house. It was almost as if they themselves were out there mingling and jostling with the crowds.

Mrs. Learner now spoke: "Your father and I agreed that there's plenty of room on the balcony in our bedroom. You can all stand and look out at what's going on, but be careful!"

An hour later the family, led by Emma, trooped into the parental bedroom. It was very cold in there – rarely was a coal fire lit in the somewhat austere bed-chamber – and when the french windows were opened with access to the balcony the temperature in the room was very nearly freezing. Emma had wisely decreed that her flock should be suitably clad and they all wore overcoats, woollen gloves, scarves and warm headgear.

John and Jim rushed to be first on the balcony; the sight which greeted them literally took their breath away.

"Golly! Look at all those people", shouted Jim, scarcely able to believe his eyes. The others took up positions further along the balcony and joined in the chorus of shouted exclamations. Peter nodded his head as if to say 'I told you so'.

"There must be at least a thousand people down there coming on foot, let alone all the others arriving by bus and char-a-bancs", he proclaimed grandly, "and look at their caps and scarves; they're all sporting the colours of their favourite team".

"Look at all those Generals parked in our roller-skating lanes", laughed John, "I wouldn't like to try skating there now, would you, Jim?" Jim shook his head. He was not looking down the hill at that moment; his eye was caught by someone waving from the balcony opposite. Ruth saw the waving at the same time. They all looked across and called out in unison: "Coo-ee, Alan!"

"It's Alan Carr, Mother", Peter Learner said, "I didn't know he was here from Colwyn Bay".

"Neither did I", replied his mother. "You must all go across when the match is over. Perhaps he'd like to come to tea tomorrow". Alan Carr was a great favourite with them all, and he stayed with the Maunders at No. 4 on very infrequent occasions. He was returning the waving with great enthusiasm.

The children had seen and remarked upon the fact that every single balcony, all the way up the hill, almost without exception, was crowded with gawping on-lookers. Quite a few had coloured flags or streamers in the colours of West Ham or Bolton Wanderers.

"There's the Chalmers at No. 16".

"Ooh, look, isn't that Philip and his sister further up the hill?"

"And look, even poor old Mr. Wilmington and Miss Wilmington have come out on their balcony".

"No sign of the Wyatt's next door. Perhaps it's too cold for them".

These and other excited remarks were made in the increasing noise and bustle of chattering football supporters and hundreds of crawling buses and motor-cars.

The youngsters' eyes goggled as they watched a dark-skinned man mingling with the crowds. He was carrying a queer-shaped wicker basket slung over his shoulder, and suddenly turned off the crowded main road to ascend the steep slope of their own Linden Avenue.

"He's coming up here", breathed Jim. The man stopped just out-side the first house in the avenue, almost immediately below them, and wearily lowered his basket onto the pavement. Several local youths, some of whom Jim and John knew well, had followed him up the hill. They watched spellbound as he sat on the kerb and slowly lit a long-stemmed pipe. Satisfied this was going well he cautiously opened the lid of his basket and murmured a few words into the interior.

Also watching, the Learner children leaned precariously over the balcony railings, despite their mother's warning, and were fasci-nated to see a huge snake uncoil itself from the bottom of the bas-ket and slither insidiously around the keeper's neck.

Peter had gone a dreadful green colour. He tore himself away from the railings and dashed into the bedroom. He couldn't stand snakes. They all looked sympathetic but soon returned to the rail-ings. The Indian man, or he certainly looked Indian, was calmly counting the copper and silver coins he had collected from the crowds. Meanwhile the snake appeared to have gone to sleep round his neck. After a few minutes the local youths, tiring of the excite-ment of watching the shiny reptile, ran off down the hill. The man put the money in a bag in the bottom of the basket — he knew it would be perfectly safe there — coaxed the snake back into the wicker basket, got up and disappeared from sight.

Mrs. Learner who had gone downstairs to prepare dinner, now

appeared with four cups of Bovril. Peter followed her in and, greenish hue gone, peeped furtively over the balcony. Satisfied the snake man had gone he took one of the cups and, like the others, gulped down the hot drink thirstily.

They then returned to their positions on the balcony, and Peter pointed out two foreign looking women, wearing brightly coloured scarves and with large brass ear-rings dangling from their ear-lobes, slowly making their way up Linden Avenue. They both carried huge baskets heavily laden with all manner of household goods. Twenty or thirty clothes pegs, all strung together, hung from the handles of the baskets.

Jim said: "Look at all those clothes pegs and pots and kettles and things. That lady (pointing at the younger of the two women), has got lots and lots of exciting things in her basket, I'll bet".

They all watched as the two women knocked at the doors of houses lower down the hill. This was probably the first time residents of Wembley Hill would have their homes invaded with the wailing insistence of wandering gipsy women. One of them carried several little bunches of purple heather in her hand. As she climbed the hill and knocked on the Maunder's door, it was opened by Mrs. Maunders.

"Buy a bunch of heather, dear, it'll bring you good luck". Mrs. Maunders shook her head. "Look, dear, fine clothes pegs, made them myself, you look a good housewife, you'll always be wanting new clothes pegs..."

Mrs. Maunders shook her head again and made to shut the front door, but the gipsy woman persisted. Peter and the others were all absorbed in watching this scene: they could see that Alan Carr was peering precariously over his balcony railings.

The woman thrust her basket against the door and brandished a small copper kettle in poor Mrs. Maunder's face. "Beautiful kettle, lady. Only two shillings, dear. You'd pay much more in the shops".

"Go away, woman", shouted the indignant Mrs. Maunders, who was getting very cross. She pushed hard on the basket and nearly sent the gipsy woman flying. "If you don't go away I shall call my husband".

With that she banged the front door firmly shut. The woman shook her fist and climbed wearily further up the hill. She and her companion would probably be lucky if any of the occupants of Linden Avenue bought anything from them at all. Like Mrs. Learner all the housewives in the avenue had to be careful how they spent their house-keeping money. They liked to browse around the shops looking for bargains and would not spend a penny until they were sure they were getting good value for their shillings and pence. Also they had an inbuilt suspicion of hawkers, salesmen and canvassers calling at the door.

When this drama had been unfolded there was a shout from Ruth "Daddy's coming — Daddy's coming — come on you three, race you downstairs". With a quick peep over the railings, John, Jim and Peter went careering down the stairs close on Ruth's heels.

Emma rushed out of the kitchen and waited her turn to embrace and be embraced by her beloved spouse. When the commotion had died down and Edward had been told all about their adventures on the balcony, he retired to his bedroom to tidy up and later joined his family round the kitchen table.

Eating his meal surrounded by his loved ones he could not possibly have imagined what dramatic events would take place that afternoon when he and his eldest son pushed through the turnstiles admitting them to the Empire Stadium.

A Memorable Trip

THERE was no doubt the very first Football Cup Final played at Wembley on 28th April 1923 was a truly great and memorable occasion. With few exceptions everybody entered into the spirit of things on this historic day.

Ordinary people like Edward and Emma, their friends and their neighbours, had been keyed up to witness all the sensational happenings, strange visitors, noises, smells and motorised and horse-drawn vehicles of every description. But the ultimate glory was the fact that the people of Wembley were playing host to their beloved Sovereign, His Majesty King George the Fifth.

Leaving the house at 12.30 p.m. Peter and his father had no sooner descended the short stretch of Linden Avenue and crossed the main road than they had no choice but to be carried along on a human tide.

"Keep close to me all the time, Peter", warned Edward, "I'm going to keep my hand on your shoulder until we're seated in the stadium".

They skirted the multitude of buses parked in their 'skating lanes'. Apart from the ubiquitous GENERALS, there were double- and single-deck Thomas Tillings, 'pirate' buses of many shapes and sizes, county buses — for example Midland County — and a few horse-drawn buses brought out of retirement for the special occasion.

They were approaching the turnstiles when they heard an extraordinary voice shouting louder than all the other voices in this sea of humanity.

"I gotta horse — I gotta horse".

Craning his neck Peter could just make out a clutch of brightly coloured feathers waving over the heads of the crowd. In a few minutes they had been jostled to within a couple of paces of the owner of voice and feathers.

"Who's that, Father? What an amazing costume and he's so tall". Peter shouted to his father over the general din.

Edward leant down to shout in Peter's ear. "That's Prince Monolulu; he's a self-styled Chief of an African tribe and he comes to many of our sporting events. He's well known particularly at horse race meetings; claims he can give you a certain winner for a small financial hand-out".

The sun had unexpectedly peeped through grey skies. The leather handled horses-tail fly swat Prince Monolulu was carrying was used to great effect, swatting imaginary flies left, right and centre. The imposing figure was soon lost to sight, repeating his familiar call, as he pushed through one of the turnstiles.

Edward paid the entrance fee for himself and his son. The authorities had decided that only a few seats needed booking in advance. This was a decision which was to be strongly regretted and criticised in the light of fearful events to come.

They had only just passed through the turnstiles when Peter caught sight of Fred Witting emerging from an adjacent entrance. He was astonished to see his school buddy, normally quiet and withdrawn, sporting a tam-o-shanter and scarf in the distinctive colours of Bolton Wanderers. He grinned hugely at Fred and waved to him, but because of the crush he was unable to speak to him.

The crowd, which was very good humoured, enjoying every moment of the anticipation of a hard-fought match, shouting bantering remarks to the wearers of colours of opposing teams and removing caps and scarves in the sudden unexpected warmth, moved slowly and shufflingly towards the great building with its twin towers proudly displaying the Royal Standard and the Union Jack. At last they were through the numerous subways or tunnel entrances leading to the main arena.

Edward dragged his son up a long flight of steps to some seats almost at the top of the stadium. They would have liked to be nearer the pitch but with the turnstiles having opened at 11.30 a.m., and as it was now nearly half past one, there were precious few seats still unoccupied.

"This way, Peter, we'll go to those two seats along the end of this row". Scrambling and pushing past the legs of seated spectators they had almost reached their intended seats when Edward saw, to his dismay, that two people from the gangway at the other end of the row had occupied the seats they were making for. Now they were stuck half way along a row and were forced to struggle back again to the original gangway.

Looking desperately around and thinking that he and Peter would have to stand during the entire match, Peter said: "Look, Father, there's somebody waving up there and I think they're waving at us".

"I think you're right; come on, boy".

Vastly relieved, they climbed more steps and were thankful to see two empty seats being kept for them by some very good neighbours. Thanking them profusely they sat down and were at last able to take stock of their surroundings.

* * * *

What immediately struck Peter was the vast area of lush greeness opened out before him. The grass at Wembley was probably nurtured and tended better than the greens at any of the top golf courses in Great Britain. It was surrounded by a running track which was laid down to international standards and was the only one in the country of that standard in 1923.

Harassed officials were moving around at the tunnel entrances and round the pitch. From this height they resembled match-stick men, running round in unco-ordinated movements and dashing from place to place. He could see that every stand was absolutely packed; the organisers had reckoned on an attendance of around 120,000 spectators.

Unknown to Edward and Peter and to the multitudes already safely inside the stadium, the authorities had given an urgent order for all gates and entrances to be closed. In fact they were almost certainly among the last to gain admission officially.

Above the noise and hubbub of everyone within the stadium could be heard an angry roar of people clamouring for entrance outside the gates. The situation was definitely becoming tense. At around two o'clock the police handling the furious crowds surging against all the entrances had been forced to telephone Scotland Yard. Their action was in vain. After another quarter of an hour the relatively few police on duty ouside the stadium were swept aside. A huge force of another 100,000 people, desperate to get into the grounds at all costs, broke through the police lines and surged onto the lovingly prepared pitch.

Officials, spectators and players waiting in the main tunnel were horrified; it looked as if the game would have to be abandoned. To make matters worse news had just come through that King George V and Queen Mary were approaching Wembley Stadium.

The atmosphere was electric. Thousands of would-be spectators were milling about on the pitch and on the running track. People in the stands all round the arena could not see a blade of grass which was not covered with a sea of humanity. The noise was indescribable. The situation had become extremely frightening, and Edward could see that Peter, even in his seat high up in the stands, had gone very quiet with the anxiety of the moment. He put a protective arm round his shoulder; if truth were known, Mr. Learner was increasingly aware that things were looking decidedly ugly.

Outside the stadium crowds of loyal subjects lined the route to watch the King and Queen. After a few minutes a great roaring ovation could be heard as the Royal party emerged from one of the tunnels. The presence of the King and his Queen standing firmly to attention in their special stand as the National Anthem played appeared to have the effect of calming the situation.

What happened next was nothing short of miraculous. A

mounted policeman seated on a white horse moved quickly amongst the milling crowds on Wembley's superb pitch. Gradually every single man, woman and child was firmly shepherded to the area behind the touchlines. There were obviously no seats available so it was decided by officials that they be permitted to sit on the ground wherever they could find space.

And now another great roar went up as the two teams, shaken but determined to give of their best, ran through the tunnel and out onto the pitch. When the whistle blew for kick-off the game was exactly 40 minutes late starting.

In the circumstances it was not expected that the huge crowd, some of whom were practically spilling onto the playing surface, would see the best football ever played. But there was genuine relief that the game could be played at all. Peter's forecast was proved hopelessly wrong. Bolton Wanderers had a magnificent 2 - 0 victory over West Ham United.

It was not until well after eight o'clock that night that the vast majority of tired but happy spectators had gone home. A few of the younger element amongst the supporters still roamed the streets but eventually they made their way to tramstop or railway station.

It was still daylight; a man who had been entertaining the crowds with tunes from his barrel-organ wearily wheeled his contraption away, but the little monkey on top chattered ceaselessly and tirelessly to anyone passing by. A company of policemen, duty done, piled into a char-a-banc parked in Dagmar Avenue. Except for empty bottles, old newspapers, abandoned football favours and other bric-a-brac, Wembley Hill Road was once again quiet and almost deserted.

But in Linden Avenue another real life drama was still to be played out that day.

* * * *

Edward and Emma Learner were having a deservedly quiet nap in the withdrawing room. After the dramatic events of the day Edward was physically and mentally drained. He and Peter had done their best to give the family a blow by blow account of their experiences that afternoon. Peter had retired to his bedroom to catch up with some homework.

Emma told Ruth, Jim and John they could stay on the balcony until half past eight. They had pleaded with her that they wanted to get the last ounce of excitement out of a marvellously exciting day.

The three of them were still waving and calling to neighbours coming up the hill or to others, like themselves, still standing on their own balconies.

Jim suddenly shouted: "Hey! Look at that car coming down the hill!" He pointed up in the direction of the Chalmers' house. "Look! There's nobody in it".

The others craned their necks and watched, horrified, as the little open two-seater motor-car gathered speed and careered past them. The front wheels were turning neither to right or left; if they had been then the car would have mounted the pavement and crashed into somebody's front wall. Now travelling at a frightening speed the car covered the remaining fifty or so feet to the bottom of the hill, shot across the main road and crashed into the railings.

A woman walking along Wembley Hill Road carrying a shopping basket had the presence of mind to stop dead in her tracks; the car could only have missed her by inches. It was nothing short of miraculous that nobody was killed or injured. Barely half an hour ago there were still quite a few people making their way homewards.

This extraordinary incident was the talk of the neighbourhood for many weeks to come.

Greatest Exhibition of All

SPRING merged into summer. On the surface life had returned to normal for the residents of Wembley Hill.

The milkman delivered the milk; Prince pawed the pavement outside Letchworth for his lumps of sugar; the main roads had long since been swept clean of Cup Final debris; roller skating was once again in full swing in the deserted bus lanes and Mrs. Jones was able to gossip with Mrs. Robinson peacefully in time honoured fashion.

Inevitably the unprecedented events of 28th April were, for a long time a subject of untiring conversation in shops, local halls, public houses, tram stops and even after church services. Knowledgeable pundits, in their superior wisdom after the event, stated that if it had not been for that dreadful pass by the right-winger just before time, Bolton Wanderers could easily have scored another goal. In the Learner household Peter had not been allowed to forget his confident forecast of a West Ham victory.

However, despite the fact that comparative peace had returned to the neighbourhood there was hectic activity in the vicinity of Raglan Gardens for many months to come. Jim had completed his last 'term', if it could be so described, at the diminutive school in Oakington Avenue run by Miss Henderson, the governess. He was now at the same school in Hindes Road, Harrow, as brother John. Peter was in his last term at the Lower School of John Lyon also in Harrow and Ruth was well established at her new school, the Harrow County for Girls.

Every day during term time, be it wet or fine, they all four walked down Raglan Gardens on their way to Wembley Park Station. They did not dawdle on the outward journey; being late at their respective schools meant writing 100 lines after school in their best hand-writing. But coming home was a different matter.

Despite being told by mother that they must come home in good time for tea, the order was not always obeyed. And could they be blamed? The extensive site in Raglan Gardens as far as the eye could see was now choc-a-block with extraordinary buildings of unimaginable variety. Peering through the wire fence bordering the grounds on which the exhibition was being built Peter and the others watched spell-bound at the comings and goings of lorries, skips, cranes, wheel-barrows, horses, carts and a host of other site vehicles the like of which the children had never seen in their lives.

Every day pavilions got higher, kiosks sprang up like mushrooms and a strange-looking railway track was being laid. It was not actually a railway track as visitors to the exhibition would see in due course. This railway was to play a dominant part in the Learner children's lives when the exhibition was opened.

In a surprisingly short time the entire area from Wembley Hill to the far corner of Wembley Park was crammed with structures of every description. There was so much activity both of men and machines, apparently being carried out in a haphazard fashion, that it was hardly surprising several buildings were not completed in time for the opening on the historic day.

People continued to go to the shops, visit the cinema, attend church services, have babies, go to funerals and, in some cases, get drunk in the 'local'. They wanted to carry on as they had always done, and were not going to be put off by a couple of dozen sweating, beefy, struggling sportsmen moving heaven and earth to get a spinning ball into the back of a string net!

But these humble citizens were destined to be witness to far more excitement than a mere Cup Final. As the summer wore on and fires began to be lit in the approaching autumn weather, the finished buildings and those still to be completed in Wembley Park heralded the most remarkable exhibition ever to be held anywhere in the world.

* * * *

April 23rd 1924 had been decided for the opening of the exhibition and when the great day dawned what could only be described as pandemonium was let loose in the area.

The Learner's quiet little township witnessed a complete metamorphosis. The entire neighbourhood was flooded with cars, char-a-bancs, buses, vans, tramcars, horse-drawn vehicles, people on foot, people on motor-bikes and people in taxis and 'cabs'. It seemed impossible that Wembley could accommodate them all. From very early in the morning until the official opening time they came and came.

Once again the balconies of Linden Avenue, Dagmar Avenue and Mostyn were packed to capacity with goggle-eyed folk. A few stout-hearted residents decided to chance their arm and join the throng making their way to the turnstiles. For them and for the thousands approaching the exhibition grounds, it would be a day forever engraved on their memories.

Within twelve months of the unforgettable events of the Football Cup Final the opening of the British Empire Exhibition took the civilised world by storm. Even the most optimistic of the officials, financial backers and organisers could not have foreseen how extremely popular this wonderful commercial and aesthetic mirror of the empire would become.

Once again cheering crowds lined the route to be taken by King George and Queen Mary. This time every man, woman and child clutched and waved a Union Jack in patriotic fervour. The roars which greeted the Royal couple could surely have been heard in the empire's capital city itself.

* * * *

It was a hard slog, in fact really hard going for Jim, but they'd managed it; all four of them. Jim had given up gob-stoppers, pear drops and a couple of issues of The Magnet. John had given up liquorice sticks and liquorice pipes for a month and didn't go to the pictures for a whole fortnight. Ruth had given up Film Weekly and her favourite sweets, Fry's Chocolate Cream, also for a month.

Father had promised them that if they saved really hard he would put some money towards buying them each a season ticket for the British Empire Exhibition. At a ceremony on the kitchen table they watched with breathless excitement as he produced four season tickets and four enamel badges, which bore the logo: 'B.E.E.'

"You'll be able to go to the exhibition whenever your household duties and homework are done to your mother's satisfaction. And you'll go in through the 'Members Only' turnstile without having to queue up". Mr. Learner smiled affectionately at his children.

They examined their season tickets and badges with unrestrained joy. They realised that they could probably go to the exhibition tomorrow and the next day and the day after that — in fact to their young minds the possibilities of going to the exhibition seemed to stretch into eternity.

Jim and John's Wonderful Day Out

"there's your sandwiches, a bar of chocolate and an apple each; you can get an orange drink or whatever you like from one of those kiosks. Have you got your sixpences and your season tickets in your pockets?" Emma looked anxiously at her two youngest sons.

IT was a glorious day in May. Ruth and Peter each had sports fixtures at their respective schools — Peter was playing cricket in the Second Eleven at John Lyon's and Ruth, for the first time, was playing in an important hockey match in her school's Third Team. They had gone off some time ago with their mother's blessing.

On this lovely sunny Saturday morning John and Jim set off with their season tickets tucked safely in their blazer pockets. In no time at all they were thrust into the hurly-burly of the Amusement Park. Here they spent one of their pennies on a magically exciting 'dodgem' ride — laughing and shouting every time they bumped into one of the other cars.

They stood and stared at the antics of shrieking girls trying to keep their balance on the cake-walk; not an easy manoeuvre — one was either jerked hard against the side of the jogging, tilting platform or thrown unceremoniously up into the air. It was not unknown for weak-stomached folk to be violently sick after their three pennyworth.

One of their greatest thrills was to go on The Whip. This fearsome-sounding machine consisted of a round bucket seat attached to a steel pole; the sides of the contraption were well padded and they needed to be! Proceeding cautiously along for a short time almost at a snail's pace, one was suddenly and terrifyingly whipped round until a circle was almost completed.

On this day John and Jim had agreed to have a go on only two of the pleasures offered to visitors. They had spent a penny on the dodgems and now they made their way to the 'helter-skelter'; this also cost a penny. The rest of their money would be spent on a ride on the famous Never Stop Railway.

Picking up their thick mats they chased each other up the internal spiral staircase of the helter-skelter, jostling and pushing with other youngsters similarly bent on getting to the top first. Stepping onto the platform in the open air some fifty feet above ground, they had a magnificent panoramic view of the exhibition. All around the outside of the conical erection was a downward spiralling runway smoothed over with constant use into a highly polished surface. It was for all the world like descending a wooden Cresta Run.

Jim was away first and John got ready to follow him, but he had not got properly seated on his mat. Halfway down the mat slid from under him and John, clutching wildly at the sides whizzing past, sped the rest of the way down the chute on his bottom. Not only was it extremely painful but he knew he would be 'in for it' from his mum.

Jim was in hysterics to see his brother's misfortune but John said: "Can't see what you're laughing at, look at my trousers and my blazer. I'm going to catch it from mum".

* * * *

The brothers now had several options open to them. They could look round many of the Palaces or Pavilions which were free admission, or wander over to the lake outside the Indian Pavilion and watch the paddle boats being taken out. But it was watching only today – taking a boat out cost threepence a trip.

They had both befriended a boatman who skippered a larger boat called the M.V. Rangoon. Occasionally, when he was in a good mood, he would smuggle one or the other of them on board for a free ride and would even let them take the tiller sometimes. But the Rangoon was silent on its moorings today.

Another option was to stand beside a tall African man on duty outside an ABDULLAH kiosk. This splendid specimen, clad in tarboosh, khaki jersey, shorts and puttees, stood with his rifle 'at ease' beside the kiosk for a period of an hour without moving a muscle. It was quite remarkable. Members of the public, emulating the gawping crowds round the sentry outside Horse Guards parade ground, would flock round the ABDULLAH man for photos to be taken.

In years to come the photo albums would be dragged from the bottom of a drawer and the bored relative would be shown a snap; 'and that's me at the Wembley Exhibition'.

Feeling thirsty Jim and John went to one of the many drinking fountains in the grounds. As it was getting quite hot they knew exactly where to go to cool off a bit, and made their way to one of the largest and certainly one of the most handsome buildings in the exhibition. The size of the building and the extent of its exhibits was hardly surprising; the Australian Pavilion represented a microcosm of the largest continent in the British Empire.

One section of this vast building was devoted entirely to sheep shearing, and in season the crowds flocked round the stand to watch experts clipping and shearing the wool off struggling livestock. Out-of-season visitors could relax for a half hour or so in the small cinema. Entrance was free and the film shown, which lasted just over half an hour, depicted every aspect of Australian farming and agriculture. It was repeated time and again during the daily opening of the pavilion.

All the Learner children came to know and love this beautiful haunting film called 'Neath Australian Skies'. Suitable poignant music accompanied the scenes of immense rolling pastures, vast herds of cattle and sheep, purple mountains and green valleys. It was a film whose evocative beauty would remain in their memories for ages to come. On this day Jim and John watched the film twice.

They had already been in the exhibition grounds for three hours and still had their threepences but the Never-Stop-Railway was to be postponed until the last moment.

Emerging from the cinema they wandered happily round the various stands in the pavilion. Almost invariably each stand in each pavilion had stacks of leaflets, booklets and other literature presenting the arts, crafts and indigenous enterprises of its corner of the empire. Poor Emma was filled with dismay at the volume of such literature brought into the house after every visit. Most of this literature was supplied gratis to the visitors.

John saw a handsome leaflet, almost a magazine, lying on the counter of the fruit growing section of the pavilion, and added this to his sheaf of leaflets. Making their way to the exit, they were just going through the door when their arms were held firmly by a uniformed pavilion official.

"Now then young gentlemen, you come along with me to the manager's office".

John looked at the tall man with surprise and sudden fear. "Hey! What's the idea? You let go of my arm". He tried to pull away from the official but the man was too strong.

Jim struggled, too, but they were no match for him. He shepherded them into an office at the back of the building.

"Well Watkins, what's all this? What've these lads been up to?" The surprisingly young-looking manager glanced at Jim and John and back at Watkins.

"I caught them stealing a magazine from the counter, sir. This young man", he pointed to John, "picked it up and put it with the other papers he's got in his hand now".

John immediately protested: "I didn't steal it, sir", he said with great indignation. "I saw it lying on the counter, like a lot of the others, and I thought it was free of charge". He looked down at the magazine which the official had taken from him and placed on the table; he could see now that '6d' was printed on the top right hand corner.

Jim was now blubbering; he thought they were probably going to be sent to prison. John, although he knew he had right on his side, began to cry too. The young manager who probably had a family of his own took pity on them.

"Now listen to me boys, unless you can pay for this, you'll have to put it back on the counter".

"We've only got threepence left, sir", John cried tearfully, "and we were going to spend that on the Never-Stop-Railway. I didn't know it was sixpence, honestly".

He gulped back his tears and they both stood miserably in front of the manager's desk. The young man smothered a smile and said to them: "Alright, I'll believe you this time, but if I catch you at anything like this again, I'll have to tell your parents about you. Now off you go".

Watkins opened the door. The two boys ran out of the office, and hastened towards the main entrance. "Gosh, I was really frightened then, John. That chap in uniform scared me a lot. I couldn't think what was going on".

"Nor could I," John said. "I'm jolly well not going in that pavilion again for a long time".

* * * *

They shook the Australian dust off their feet and made their way to the nearest 'station' of their beloved railway. In the carefree manner of youth they quickly forgot their terrors as they approached the ticket office. Paying the necessary 3d. each for the journey they waited at the station platform for the next carriage to come along. It was not really a platform at all; merely a concrete slab on which passengers stood as they boarded one of the carriages.

This remarkable railway was only one of four types of transport within the exhibition grounds. The Never-Stop (so called because it literally never stopped) ran from north to south of the grounds, a Road-Rail system ran from the west to the east, the Railodok cars ran from one point to another on circular tours and finally 300 to 400 bath chairs were on hire at 2s. 6d. an hour. There was no doubt the Never-Stop was the favourite with the visitors (and with the boys).

It carried up to 15,000 people daily, and consisted of a series of small covered coaches looking not unlike cable cars used in Swiss ski-ing resorts. They were given momentum by a form of continuously revolving spiral steel screws, which functioned in a deep pit underneath the coaches. The coach speed varied according to the elongation or closeness of the screw thread. At stations which were spaced every few hundred yards along the route, the coaches moved very slowly — slow enough for passengers to board the vehicles in comparative safety.

They then picked up speed and were able to travel at anything up to 24 miles per hour. The Learner children found it tremendously fascinating and Jim and John — the Australian incident now forgotten — knew without doubt the ride on the Never-Stop was going to be the highlight of their day.

Literature and lunch packs clutched firmly in hot sticky hands they eagerly awaited an oncoming coach. "Come on, Jim, race you to be first on board". John darted to the side of the coach before it had really got to the station and clambered aboard. Jim was only seconds behind him. They slithered breathlessly onto a seat and sat side by side in an empty coach, laughing as a crowd of foreign visitors watched with amusement the antics of two young English schoolboys.

Jim opened his paper bag and cried out: "Oh look, squashed banana sandwiches. Dear Mummy, she knows they're our favourite".

John had already started on his. He knew that to be able to play their special time-honoured game, they must finish one sandwich before they got to the next station. Arriving there they leapt out of the coach and immediately boarded the one which was slowing down right behind them. This was repeated again and again, each time consuming (or gobbling down) another sandwich, a slab of cake, a bar of chocolate or whatever happened to be in their lunch pack. It was great fun and they changed coaches as often as they liked.

Their final change had taken them to the terminus where the coaches turned on a sixpence and started back the other way. Tired, but ecstatically happy, they faced the long trek home buoyed up by their wonderful adventures.

Goodbye to Wembley Hill

O N 1st November 1924 the exhibition closed. From 23rd April until the closing date, 17,403,119 visitors paid to see the greatest show of all time. But the powers that be were not convinced that it had been an unqualified success.

Doubts were expressed as to whether it could be held the following year. However, trusting in providence and with the various pavilions better equipped and better managed than previously, it reopened on 9th May 1925. But an unusually wet summer, combined with the novelty of the exhibition having worn off, resulted in its final closure on 31st October. The attendance was well down on 1924.

There was absolutely no question of holding the exhibition on the next or any subsequent year. Endless arguments ensued as to what should be done with the multitude of constructions now lying idle. The pavilions, palaces, the amusement park, kiosks, rolling stock of the three rail networks, the lake in front of the Indian Pavilion and all the other paraphernalia of a one-time successful exhibition had to be disposed of.

Concurrently the stadium, which had been used during 1924 for a variety of activities – choirs, firework displays, pageants and a rodeo – was also the subject of heated discussions as to its future. There was no disagreement on one very important point; the Wembley Stadium was to be the venue for the Football Cup Final for the next few years and for the forseeable future.

As for the exhibition site, the citizens of Wembley followed a variety of reports in local and national newspapers. One newspaper suggested that the entire site could become a vast garden suburb. A well-known film producer favoured the idea of turning the area into a British Hollywood. Many other ideas were dismissed out of hand on the grounds of being financially unsound.

Eventually thousands of people from all walks of life were saddened at the final decision that some beautiful buildings, such as the Bermuda Pavilion with its aesthetic bridges and gardens, and many others, were to be declared fit only for factories and stores.

Arthur Elvin, who had worked in the exhibition first in one of the kiosks and then in a managerial capacity, was contracted to demolish most of the smaller buildings. In years to come the name of Sir Arthur Elvin was to become synonymous the world over with Wembley and particularly with the Stadium.

The final decision to demolish most of the exhibition buildings was a minor tragedy. The uniqueness of the entire vast enterprise was a spectacle which had fired the imagination of so many millions of people.

* * * *

Whatever the future of the stadium or the exhibition, Mr. Learner continued to catch the same train to the City every weekday morning. He turned out hundreds of overalls and boiler suits, smoked too many cigarettes, played the piano as often as he could, attended classical concerts at London's Queens Hall and worshipped every Sunday with unfailing regularity.

On the surface he was well content with his life, but lurking beneath was the nagging suspicion that all was not well with his family.

Discussing matters with his wife, sometimes at night before dropping off to sleep, or enjoying a quiet chat when the children had been packed off to bed, as now, he told her of his concern.

"I'm afraid our own quiet little neighbourhood will never be the same again, my dear. The coming of the exhibition with all its ramifications, the people, some undesirable, out and about in our streets and the effect some of them are having on our dear children, are beginning to worry me very much".

They were drinking a last cup of tea in the kitchen before their own bedtime. "Although the exhibition is finished we don't know yet what will replace it in the exhibition grounds. With all this talk of a garden suburb, film studios and other grandiose schemes, there are bound to be these undesirables in the neighbourhood for a long time to come". Emma nodded: "This worries me too, Edward, In fact Jim told me only yesterday he was spoken to by a man in Aeroplane Road" She paused as she saw her husband's alarmed expression. "I didn't want to worry you; the man offered him some sweets but Jim said he ran off up the hill and into Wembley Park Station".

"There you are, that's exactly the sort of thing I mean", Edward said angrily. "I've drummed it into our dear ones over and over again never to speak to strangers. But it is an ever present danger now, today, and looks like remaining that way".

"Yes", Emma said, "and when you think, it was only a couple of years ago, before the stadium and exhibition, that they were unlikely to encounter anybody except the postman, the milkman and the baker's roundsman".

Her husband sighed: "Those things are quite enough to worry about without wondering what's going to happen here in our own home".

"You mean, how we're going to manage here with the children growing up so fast?"

"Exactly". Edward nodded. "There are so many things here in this house that I am not happy about".

"I know exactly what you mean and I haven't told you this, dearest, but Ruth said to me a few days ago that she thought it was rotten we had to go on living in this doll's house and when were we going to move to somewhere nicer!"

Edward laughed grimly. "That is the result of her mixing with her friends from the Harrow County School. Nevertheless that's just another instance of the sort of thing I'm getting worried about".

He got up wearily from the table and started the identical routine of closing up for the night that he had followed for the last fifteen

173

years. He banked up the fire in the kitchen range, checked all the downstairs windows, locked and bolted front and back doors, turned off gas mantles in kitchen and scullery and cleaned and polished his shoes ready for the morning. Looking round to see that everything was to his satisfaction, he plodded slowly up the stairs.

* * * *

Another four years passed. Peter, now a tall thin upright young man in his twentieth year, was learning the intricacies of the insurance world. He had matriculated with distinction at his old school and taken the Junior Cambridge examination; every school report spoke of a promising career for this serious-minded boy.

Ruth, although known to be unenthusiastic in her scholastic efforts, did well enough at school, and was thought suitable for a position as junior clerk at the Prudential Assurance Company in Holborn.

John was progressing very satisfactorily at the Lower School of John Lyon despite the fact that he had fallen foul of the French master for facetiousness; his sights were set on the legal profession. For a time he and Jim were co-pupils at this school when the latter finished at Quainton Hall School in Hindes Road.

Jim was a bit of a rolling stone. A four-year apprenticeship in a London store was followed by a further year in a well-known sports emporium in Piccadilly. At some time in the future the plan was for him to join forces with his father in the City factory. Sadly this arrangement was to be abruptly terminated with the advent of the Second World War. Jim joined forces of a very different nature in 1940, and eventually a career in the Civil Service was opened up for the youngest member of the Learner family.

All four children were genuinely grateful to their father who had paid for their private education at much financial sacrifice to himself.

* * * *

On a beautiful summer day in 1929 the removal van came and took away the entire contents of Letchworth.

174

Henry and Harriet Wyatt, the Maunders, the Chalmers, the Presses and the woman who looked as if she had 'dipped her face in the flour bin', all congregated outside the Learner's home to bid the family a fond farewell. It was sad but inevitable; Letchworth was almost bursting at the seams.

Mr. Learner had at last been able to save enough money to buy larger, more commodious premises in a very pleasant area some four or five miles north of Harrow. Letchworth had never been his own; he had rented it for the entire period of his tenancy. When he left the old house where he and his little family had been so happy, he did not have a penny to show for it.

There were inevitable regrets as the removal van rolled down Linden Avenue. Memories of parading round the bandstand in King Edward the Seventh's park, playing french cricket in their tiny little garden, walking down Raglan Gardens to the 'Boo-Boo' place, feeding dear greedy old Prince (now long since gone to his final pasture) and listening to father playing evocative music on his beloved piano.

All these and a thousand other memories flitted through their minds as the van disappeared round the corner into Wembley Hill Road. But each member of the Learner family knew in his or her heart that the glorious, golden days of their dear old beloved Wembley Hill had gone forever.